AS
LEVEL

PHYSICS QUESTIONS
FOR CCEA AS LEVEL

COLOURPOINT
EDUCATIONAL

Rewarding Learning

Pat Carson and Roy White

Published 2016 by Colourpoint Creative Limited

© 2016 Pat Carson, Roy White and
   Colourpoint Creative Ltd

ISBN: 978-1-78073-036-3

First Edition
First Impression

Layout and design: April Sky Design, Newtownards

Colourpoint Educational
An imprint of Colourpoint Creative Ltd
Colourpoint House
Jubilee Business Park
21 Jubilee Road
Newtownards
County Down
Northern Ireland
BT23 4YH

Tel: 028 9182 0505
Fax: 028 9182 1900
E-mail: info@colourpoint.co.uk
Web site: www.colourpoint.co.uk

The Authors

Roy White taught Physics to A level for over
30 years in Belfast. He works for an examining
body as Chair of Examiners for Double Award
Science, Principal Examiner for GCSE Physics and
Principal Examiner for A level Life and Health
Sciences. In addition to this text, he has been the
author or co-author of three successful books
supporting the work of science teachers in
Northern Ireland.

Pat Carson has been teaching Physics to A level for
over 30 years in Belfast and Londonderry. He
works for an examining body as Chief Examiner
for GCSE Physics. In addition to this text, he has
been co-author on a number of books supporting
the work of Physics teachers at AS and A2 level.

Rewarding Learning

Approved/endorsed by CCEA on 1 May 2016. If in any
doubt about the continuing currency of CCEA
endorsement, please contact Heather Clarke at CCEA,
29 Clarendon Road, Belfast, BT1 3BG.

Whilst the publisher has taken all reasonable care in the
preparation of this book CCEA makes no representation,
express or implied, with regard to the accuracy of the
information contained in this book. CCEA does not
accept any legal responsibility or liability for any errors
or omissions from the book or the consequences
thereof.

This book has been written to help students preparing
for the 2016 AS Level Physics specification from CCEA.
While Colourpoint Creative Limited and the authors
have taken every care in its production, we are not able
to guarantee that the book is completely error-free.
Additionally, while the book has been written to closely
match the CCEA specification, it the responsibility of
each candidate to satisfy themselves that they have fully
met the requirements of the CCEA specification prior to
sitting an exam set by that body. For this reason, and
because specifications change with time, we strongly
advise every candidate to avail of a qualified teacher and
to check the contents of the most recent specification for
themselves prior to the exam. Colourpoint Creative
Limited cannot be held responsible for any errors or
omissions in this book or any consequences thereof.

Note: it is the responsibility of teachers and lecturers to
carry out an appropriate risk assessment when planning
any practical activity. Where it is appropriate, they
should consider reference to CLEAPPS guidance.

Contents

Unit 1.1 (AS 1)
Physical quantities

1. Express the following physical quantities in base units:
   - (a) Gravitational potential energy
   - (b) Density
   - (c) Pressure   (Pressure is the force acting per unit area)
   - (d) Weight
   - (e) Impulse   (Impulse is the product of force and time)

2. (a) Express electrical resistance in base units (the volt is defined as joule per coulomb and the coulomb is defined as current multiplied by time).
   - (b) The temperature rise $\Delta\theta$ when an object is heated is given by the equation

   $$\Delta\theta = \frac{Q}{mc}$$

   where Q is the quantity of heat energy supplied, m is the mass of the object in kg and c is a constant known as the specific heat capacity. Derive the base units of c.

3. The motion of a vibrating object is known as simple harmonic motion. The acceleration a of the object is given by the equation

   $$a = (2\pi f)^2\, x$$

   where x is distance from a fixed point and f is the frequency of vibration.
   Show that the right hand side of the equation has the units of acceleration.

4. The strength of a material is measured by a term known as Young's modulus, E. Young's modulus is calculated by the equation:

   $$E = \frac{stress}{strain}.$$

   Stress is defined as force per unit area and strain is the ratio of the extension of a material to its original length. Determine the base units of Young's modulus.

5. The radius of a proton is 0.9 fm and its mass is 1.67×10^{-27} kg. Calculate the density, in kg m^{-3}, of the nuclear material that makes up the proton.

6. The energy released in nuclear explosions is often given in terms of thousands of tons of a conventional explosive known as TNT (1 kT = 1000 tons of TNT). The energy release of 1 kT is approximately 4.2 TJ. In 1961 the Soviet Union detonated a nuclear device with an energy release of 50 MT. Calculate the energy release of this device in J.

7. Some countries still use a system based on the inch, pound and second.
   - (a) A *thou* is $\frac{1}{1000}$ of an inch. One inch is equal to 2.54 cm.

     Calculate the number of microns (μm) in 1 *thou*.

(b) The *poundal* is the unit of force when the pound (lb) is the unit of mass. A one pound mass will accelerate at one foot per second squared when pushed by a one poundal force. Calculate the number of newtons in one poundal. 1 lb = 16 ounces (oz). 1 kg = 2 lb 3.274 oz. 1 foot = 12 inches.

8. Astronomical distances are so large that other units of measuring distance are used. 1 *astronomical unit* (AU) is equal to the average distance between the Earth and the Sun. 1 AU = 1.496×10^8 km. A *parsec* (pc) is the distance at which 1 AU will subtend an angle of 1 second of arc (see diagram).

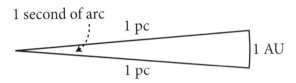

1 complete circle = 360° or 2π radians (symbol rad).
1° = 60 minutes of arc, written as 60'.
1 minute of arc (1') = 60 seconds of arc, written as 60".

A *light year* (ly) is the distance light travels in one year. The speed of light is 3×10^8 ms^{-1}.
Calculate the number of light years equivalent to 1 pc.

9. In high energy physics the probability of collisions between particles is measured in units known as *barns* (symbol b). Barns are measured in units of area. 1 b = 100 fm^2.
(a) Give 1 b in m^2.
(b) The probability of an alpha particle being scattered by a nucleus of a gold atom at a certain angle has been calculated to be 100 b. Treating the gold nucleus as a circular target for the alpha particle, calculate its radius based on this information.

10. In the SI system of units mass (M), length (L) and time (T) were chosen as base physical quantities. Imagine that instead force (F), acceleration (A) and time (T) had been chosen as the base physical quantities. What would be the base units of energy in this case?

11. A *nautical mile* is defined the distance around the equator equal to 1 minute of arc (1'). The equatorial radius of the Earth is 6378 km. A *knot* is defined as a speed of one nautical mile per hour. 1° = 60 minutes of arc, written as 60'.
(a) What is 1 nautical mile in km?
(b) Convert 15 knots to ms^{-1}.

12. The wavelength of light is sometimes given in units known as *angstroms* (symbol Å).
(a) A green line in the spectrum of mercury has wavelength of 546.047 nm or 5460.47 Å. Express 1 Å in m.
(b) Red light has a wavelength of 630 nm. What is this wavelength in angstroms?

Unit 1.2 (AS 1)
Scalars and vectors

1. (a) Distinguish between scalar and vector quantities.
    (b) Give three examples of each type of quantity, stating the SI unit in which each is measured.
    (c) The diagram shows a force of 25 N acting at 42° to the x-direction. Calculate its components in the x and y directions.

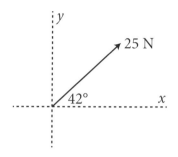

2. Two forces of 12 N and 16 N act at right angles to each other and in the directions shown in the diagram. Calculate the resultant of these two vectors and the angle it makes with the x-direction.

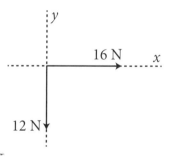

3. (a) An aircraft flies due north for 400 km then due east for 300 km. Calculate the displacement of the aircraft from its starting position. Illustrate your answer with an appropriate vector diagram.
    (b) Raindrops fall vertically with a speed of 4 ms^{-1} in still air. Calculate the angle they make with the vertical when the wind is blowing horizontally at 6 ms^{-1}. Illustrate your answer with an appropriate vector diagram.

4. The diagram shows two forces of 5 N and 8 N acting at 120° to each other. Calculate the resultant of these two forces and state its direction relative to the 5 N force. Illustrate your answer with an appropriate vector diagram.

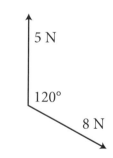

5. The diagram shows a block resting on a slope. Copy the diagram. Mark on your copy the weight of the block. The block weighs 15 N. Calculate the component of the weight at right angles to the slope and the component of the weight along the slope. Mark these components and their values on your diagram.

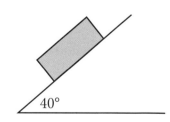

6. An object of weight W is suspended by two cables and is in equilibrium, as shown in the diagram. What is the ratio of the tensions T_1:T_2 in the cables?

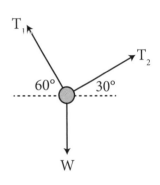

7. Find the resultant of the two forces shown in the diagram.

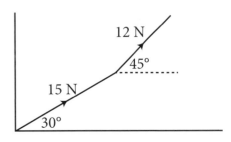

8. A hot air balloon is tethered as shown in the diagram. The balloon weighs 4000 N and the upward force on the balloon is 5000 N. The wind blowing from the left exerts a force of 500 N on the balloon. The balloon is in equilibrium. Calculate the tension in the cable.

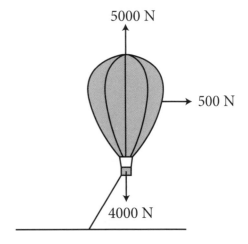

9. An aircraft makes the journey shown in the diagram. It takes off at A and finally arrives at D. Calculate its final displacement from A.

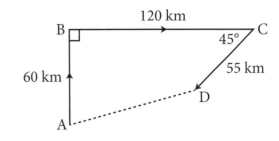

10. Vector A has a magnitude of 5 and vector B has a magnitude of 4. Their directions are at right angles to each other as shown in the diagram. In each case below draw a diagram to show the resultant vector and mark the angle the resultant makes with one of the other vectors.

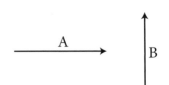

   (a) A + B
   (b) A – B
   (c) 2A – 3B
   (d) –3A + 2B

11. An aircraft is initially detected on radar at a distance of 1200 m, 40° above the horizontal, as shown in the diagram. The monitoring is stopped when the aircraft is 2000 m from the radar station. Calculate the displacement XY of the aircraft.

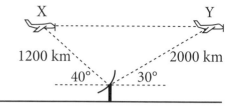

12. A motor boat sets off to cross a river. It steers at 60° to the bank as shown. The river has a current of speed 3 ms⁻¹. At what speed should it move so that the resultant of the two speeds is in the direction shown?

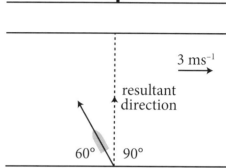

Unit 1.3 (AS 1)
Principle of moments

1. A non-uniform rod of mass 12.0 kg and length 2.00 m is pivoted at a point P at one end of the rod. The rod is held horizontally by an upward form of 50.0 N as shown in the diagram. Calculate the position of the centre of gravity. Give your answer as the distance the centre of gravity is from the point P.

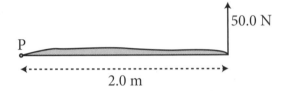

2. A patient has a leg in plaster which is supported by a sling system as shown in the diagram. The mass of the patient's leg and plaster cast is 14 kg. Calculate the suspended weight needed to hold the patient's leg in the horizontal. The leg pivots about the point P, and the centre of gravity of the leg and plaster is at point G.

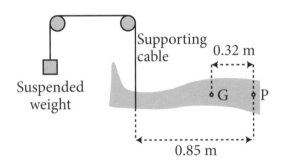

3. (a) Explain what is meant by the moment of a force about a point.
    (b) The diagram shows a gate with hinges at A and B. A steel wire CD helps support the gate. The gate weighs 500 N. The centre of gravity of the gate is at its geometrical centre. The horizontal component of the force exerted at hinge A is zero.
        (i) Calculate the distance AC.
        (ii) Calculate the tension in the wire CD.
        (iii) Calculate the magnitude and direction of the horizontal component of the force exerted on the gate by hinge B.
        (iv) Calculate the total vertical force exerted by hinges A and B.

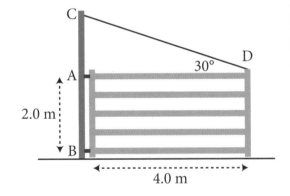

4. A double-handled wrench is used open a valve. The moment needed to do this is 22.4 Nm. This is achieved by applying two equal and opposite forces of 64 N as shown in the diagram. Calculate the distance between the two forces.

5. A uniform beam is 4.0 m long and weighs 500 N. It is hinged at one end and a cable is attached at the other end. The beam is in equilibrium.
   (a) Calculate the tension in the cable.
   (b) Calculate the resultant force at the hinge and give its direction.

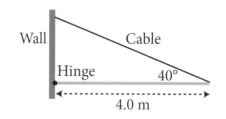

6. A painter stands on a uniform plank of length 4 m supported at two places as shown. The painter has a mass of 80 kg and the plank weighs 400 N.
   (a) Calculate the reaction (upward) forces at the supports at points A and B.
   (b) The painter moves towards the end Y. How far from end Y can the painter stand before the plank starts to tilt?

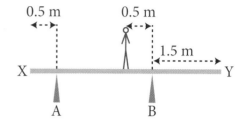

7. The diagram shows a L-shaped lever.
   (a) Calculate the resultant moment.
   (b) By how much must the 50 N force change to have the lever in equilibrium?

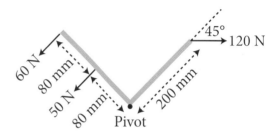

8. The diagram shows the force acting on the pedal of a bicycle. The moment of the force about the centre O is 50 Nm.
   (a) Calculate the force required to produce this moment.
   (b) Explain the advantage of moving the pedal so that the force is applied at right angles to the crank. Support your answer with an appropriate calculation.

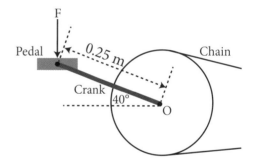

9. A metre rule is pivoted at the 30 cm mark as shown in the diagram. Weighs and forces act at the positions shown. If the metre rule is in equilibrium, calculate its weight.

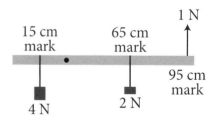

10. A *steelyard* was used for many centuries to measure weights of salt or flour. The counterweight is moved along the arm until the steelyard is balanced. The weight of the salt or flour can then be read off the scale. The distance between the pivot and the pan holding the salt or flour is fixed at 1 cm. In a particular version the counterweight has a mass of 10 g and the separation of marks on the long arm 2 cm. Calculate the smallest difference in mass that this steelyard can measure.

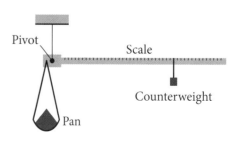

11. The diagram shows a mobile made of two identical strips each of length 40 cm and weight W.
    (a) Strip B is in equilibrium. Calculate its weight W.
    (b) Strip A is also in equilibrium. Calculate the force F.

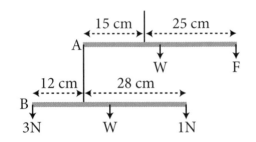

12. A metre rule of weight 3 N is pivoted at the 60 cm mark. A weight W is placed 30 cm from the pivot and the metre rule is balanced when a 6 N weight is placed 25 cm from the pivot.

    (a) Calculate the value of the weight W.

    When the weight W is placed in water the 6 N weight has to be moved to 20 cm from the pivot to have the metre rule balanced.

    (b) Calculate the upthrust on the weight W due to the water.

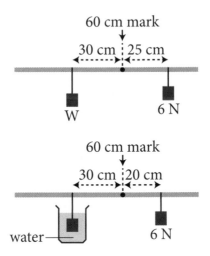

Unit 1.4 (AS 1)
Linear motion

1. An object moves in a circle of radius 5 m. It takes 10 seconds to complete one orbit.
    (a) Calculate the distance travelled by the object and its final displacement.
    (b) Calculate the average speed of the object.
    (c) Calculate the average velocity of the object, explain how you arrived at your answer.

2. (a) An object is dropped for a height of 50 m. Ignoring air resistance, calculate the time taken to reach the ground and its velocity as it hits the ground.
    (b) A helicopter is ascending at 5 ms^{-1}. When it is 200 m above the ground an object is dropped from the helicopter. Calculate the following:
        (i)   the maximum height reached by the object,
        (ii)   the time it takes from leaving the helicopter to reaching the ground.
        (iii) its velocity when it is 100 m above the ground.

3. A ball is allowed to roll, from rest, down a slope. The time it takes to travel various distances down the slope is recorded. The results of this study are shown in the table below.

Distance/m	0.5	1.0	1.5	2.0	2.5
Time/s	0.7	1.0	1.2	1.4	1.6

    (a) By plotting a suitable graph, determine the acceleration of the ball down the slope.
    (b) Calculate the average velocity and final velocity of the ball.

4. A marble is released from rest down a runway that changes as shown in the diagram. Sketch graphs to show how does the velocity and acceleration vary with time. Mark on your graphs the points A, B and C.

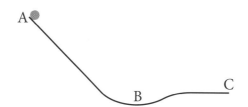

5. The velocity–time graph shows the motion of an object for a period of 10 seconds. Estimate the the distance travelled during the 10.0 s.

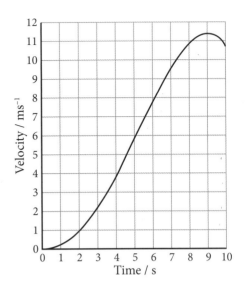

6. A particle starts at O and moves along a straight line. The velocity–time graph of its motion is shown. At the end of 10 s, determine its final position relative to the point O.

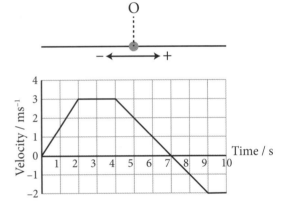

7. Three cars are involved in a race of distance 1000 m. Car A crosses the start line with an initial velocity of 20 ms⁻¹ which remains constant throughout the race. Car B starts from rest and accelerates at 1.0 ms⁻² throughout the race. Car C crosses the start line with an initial velocity of 2 ms⁻¹ and accelerates at 0.6 ms⁻² throughout the race.
   (a) Which car wins the race?
   (b) Determine the distance travelled by the two other cars when the winning car crosses the finish line.

8. A displacement–time is shown opposite. Sketch the corresponding velocity–time graph indicating relevant values of velocity and time.

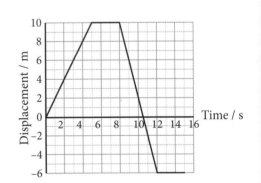

9. An object is projected vertically upwards with an initial velocity of 15 ms^{-1}. Calculate its height above the ground and its velocity after 2.2 s.

10. The diagram shows the stopping distance for a car travelling at 112 km h^{-1} (approx 70 mph).
    (a) Calculate the reaction time of the driver used to determine the thinking distance.
    (b) Calculate the deceleration used to determine the braking distance.

    $\xrightarrow{\hspace{2cm}}$ 21 m $\quad$ 75 m $\quad$ Total 96 m

    → Thinking distance
    → Braking distance

11. Two cars start moving from rest at the same time. Car A accelerates at 1.5 ms^{-2} for 10 s and then travels at a constant speed for 30 s. Car B accelerates at 1.0 ms^{-2} for 12 s and then travels at a constant velocity for 28 s.
    (a) How far has each car travelled after 40 s?
    (b) Calculate the separation of the two cars at this time, and which has travelled further.
    (c) Sketch the velocity–time graph for each car.

12. An object falls with an initial velocity from a height of 50 m.
    It strikes the ground with a velocity of 40 ms^{-1}.
    (a) Calculate the initial velocity of the object.
    (b) Calculate the time taken for the object to fall 50 m.

Unit 1.5 (AS 1)
Dynamics

1. A man runs across a rooftop and attempts to reach the roof of a neighbouring building as shown in the diagram. Calculate the minimum speed he must run at to make a successful jump.

    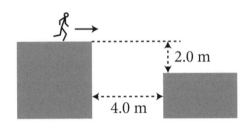

2. A cannon ball is fired at a ship. The initial velocity of the cannon ball is u and the angle of projection is θ.

    (a) Derive an expression to find the time T for the cannon ball to reach the maximum height.
    (b) Derive an expression to find the time T_{of} taken for the cannon ball to reach the ship.
    (c) Derive an expression for the horizontal distance R to the ship.
        (Remember: 2sinθcosθ = sin2θ)
    (d) If the initial velocity of the cannon ball is 90 ms⁻¹ and the ship is 600 m away, show that two angles of projection that would allow the cannon ball to hit the ship are 23.3° and 66.7°.
        (Remember: if sin 2θ = 0.5, then 2θ = 30° and 150°, so θ = 15° and 75°.)

3. A projectile fired with a velocity of 30 ms⁻¹ at an angle of 40° to the horizontal. Calculate the following:

    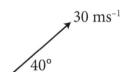

    (a) The initial vertical and horizontal components of this initial velocity.
    (b) The total time spent in the air (the time of flight).
    (c) The maximum vertical height reached by the projectile.
    (d) The range, i.e. the horizontal distance travelled by the projectile.
    (e) The angle the projectile makes with horizontal 3.0 s after it is projected. Is it moving up or down at this time?

4. A ball is kicked so that at its highest point of its path, it just clears a fence a few metres away. The fence is 2.2 m high. The ball has an initial velocity of 8.0 ms⁻¹. Show that if the ball just clears the fence, the angle of projection of the ball is 55°.

    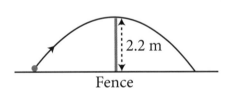

5. The projectile shown opposite has an initial velocity of 40 ms⁻¹. Calculate:
    (a) The maximum height reached above the sea.
    (b) The velocity when it strikes the sea.

    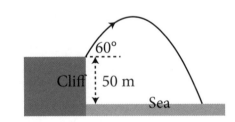

6. A ball is rolled horizontally from the top a cliff. The stone is released 25.0 m above the sea with an initial velocity of 12 ms⁻¹. Calculate:
   (a) The taken to reach the sea.
   (b) The horizontal distance from the edge of the cliff to where it strikes the sea.
   (c) The velocity of the ball when it reaches the sea.

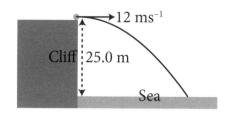

7. A projectile is released with an initial velocity of 30 ms⁻¹. It is intended to hit a target 50 m away.
   (a) Calculate the two angles of projection that would allow this to happen.
       (Hint: Use the same process as set out in Question 2.)
   (b) Explain why this projectile would not hit a target 100 m away.

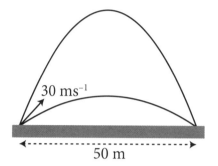

8. A projectile is fired from a gun in a downward direction from the top of a cliff as shown opposite. The projectile leaves the gun with an initial velocity of 40 ms⁻¹ at an angle of 30° below the horizontal. Calculate:
   (a) The time taken to reach the horizontal region below the cliff.
   (b) The range.
   (c) The velocity of the projectile 2.0 s after it was fired. Draw a vector diagram to show the velocity and its horizontal and vertical components.

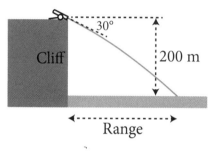

9. A projectile is fired at 50° to the horizontal with an initial velocity of 40 ms⁻¹. After 2.5 s calculate the following:
   (a) the horizontal and vertical components of its velocity,
   (b) the velocity of the projectile
   (c) its height above the ground.

10. A rescue aircraft drops a rescue capsule to a person in the sea. The aircraft is flying horizontally at 100 ms⁻¹. It takes the rescue capsule 8 s to reach the sea by the person.
    (a) Calculate the height H of the aircraft.
    (b) Calculate the velocity of the rescue capsule when it reaches the water.
    (c) Calculate the horizontal distance D shown on the diagram.

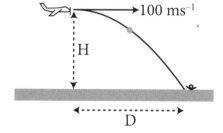

11. A projectile is projected at an of 50° to the horizontal, with an initial velocity of 35 ms⁻¹.
    (a) Calculate the two times when the vertical velocity of the projectile is 18.0 ms⁻¹.
    (b) For each time calculate the horizontal displacement of the projectile.

12. Two projectiles A and B are projected at the same time. Projectile A has an initial velocity of 20 ms⁻¹ and an angle of projection of 60°. Projectile B has an angle of projection of 45°.
    (a) Calculate the projection velocity of B if A and B reach their maximum heights at the same time.
    (b) If projectile B is to have the same range as projectile A, what velocity of projection does B need to have?

Unit 1.6 (AS 1)
Newton's laws of motion

1. A toy car is placed on a slope as shown and released. The mass of the toy car is 400 g. The frictional force between the toy and the surface is 1.20 N.
   (a) Calculate the initial acceleration of the car.

   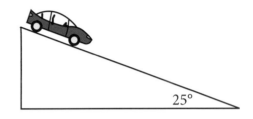

   As the toy car accelerates, air resistance causes the frictional forces to increase. At one point the frictional force has increased by 0.46 N.
   (b) Describe what effect this increase has on the acceleration of the toy.

2. Newton's Third Law deals with pairs of forces known as action and reaction.
   (a) What do you understand by action and reaction? Illustrate your answer by discussing how these terms apply to:
   (i) A tractor pulling a trailer;
   (ii) The Sun exerting a gravitational force on the Earth.
   (b) The Third Law is often stated in words as "*action and reaction are equal and opposite*". Suggest a more precise statement of the law.

3. A water skier of mass 70 kg is pulled along by a speed boat of mass 850 kg. The resistive force on the water skier is 75 N and the resistive force on the speed boat is 250 N. At one stage the acceleration of the water skier is 3.4 ms⁻². Calculate the forward force provided by the speed boat.

   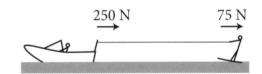

4. Two blocks of wood are linked by a light inextensible length of string. A force of 20 N is used to pull the blocks along a frictionless surface.
   (a) Calculate the acceleration of the blocks when they are released.
   (b) Calculate the tension in the string linking the two blocks.

   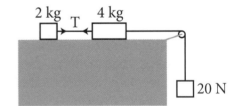

5. Two objects collide. Use Newton's Second Law and Third Law to show that linear momentum is conserved.

   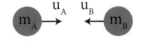

6. A conveyor belt is moving horizontally with a constant velocity of 8 ms⁻¹. Sand from a hopper above the belt drops onto the conveyor at the rate of 10 kgs⁻¹, with negligible vertical velocity. Calculate the additional force that must be provided by the motor driving the belt to maintain the constant speed of 8 ms⁻¹.

   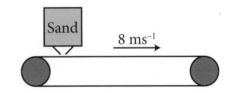

7. A cyclist and her bicycle have a mass of 80 kg. Her motion is resisted by a constant force of 10 N due to friction in the bicycle and by a variable force due to air resistance. The force due to air resistance is given by $0.15v^2$ N, where v is her velocity.
    (a) When moving at 10 ms^{-1} she exerts a force of 50 N. Calculate the acceleration this produces.
    (b) The maximum force she can exert is 100 N. Calculate the maximum speed she can reach.

8. (a) State how Newton's First Law of Motion applies to an object moving with constant velocity.
    (b) Without giving an equation state Newton's Second Law of Motion.
    (c) A spacecraft lifts off from the moon where the acceleration of free fall is 1.62 ms^{-2}. The spacecraft has an upward acceleration of 0.5 ms^{-2} at lift off. What is the force on an astronaut in the spaceship who has a weight of 750 N on the earth?

9. The diagram shows a passenger in a lift. The passenger has a mass of 65 kg. The lift has a mass of 300 kg. The lift moves from the ground floor of a building with an initial acceleration of 0.3 ms^{-2}. The lift is supported by 4 cables.
    (a) Calculate the tension in each cable.
    (b) Calculate the upward force acting on the passenger.

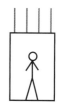

10. Five forces act on an object as shown in the diagram. The mass of the object is 4.0 kg. Calculate the magnitude and direction of the acceleration produced.

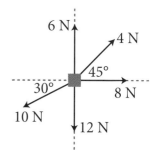

11. Two objects are connected by a light string that passes over a pulley. When released the objects accelerate.
    (a) Calculate the acceleration of the objects.
    (b) Calculate the tension in the string.

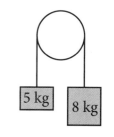

12. A car is travelling along a horizontal surface at 20 ms^{-1}. The engine provides a forward force of 2000 N. It then begins to climb a hill with a slope that rises 1 m vertically for every 10 m along the road. The car has a mass of 1500 kg. Assuming that the frictional forces opposing the motion remain constant, calculate the force that the engine must produce to give an initial acceleration of 0.5 ms^{-2} up the hill.

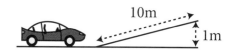

Unit 1.7 (AS 1)
Linear momentum and impulse

1. The diagram shows two wooden blocks A and B sitting on a frictionless surface. A bullet is fired at block A. The bullet has a of mass 5 g and velocity of 300 ms^{-1}. Both blocks A and B have a mass of 0.5 kg. The bullet embeds itself in block A causing it to move. Block A collides with and sticks to block B. They then move together. Calculate:

   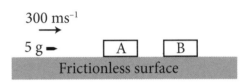

   (a) The velocity of block A after it is struck by the bullet.
   (b) The velocity of blocks A and B then they move off together.
   (c) Show by calculation that both events are examples of an inelastic collision.

2. A car of mass 1200 kg travelling at 13.5 ms^{-1} (30 mph) collides with a tree. The duration of the collision is 0.3 s.

   (a) Calculate the impulse exerted by the tree on the car.
   (b) The driver of mass 60 kg is wearing a seatbelt. The seatbelt stretches by 10 cm during the collision. Calculate the deceleration of the driver and the average force acting on the driver during the collision.
   (c) If the driver was not wearing a seatbelt they would hit their head against the windscreen and they would come to rest a distance of only 2 cm. Calculate the average force acting on the driver in this case.

3. A railway carriage of mass 3000 kg moving with a constant speed of 2 ms^{-1} collides with another carriage of mass 2500 kg which is at rest. The two carriages become coupled together. They then collide with another carriage of mass 5000 kg moving in the opposite direction with a velocity of 5 ms^{-1}. All three carriages become coupled and move together. Calculate the final velocity of the three carriages and state the direction in which they move.

   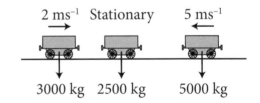

4. The *ion drive* has been proposed as a power source for spacecraft. In such a system ions are fired backwards.
   (a) Explain how this provides a thrust for a spacecraft.

   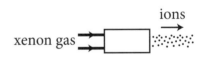

   In one such system it is proposed to use xenon ions of mass 2.2 × 10^{-25} kg with a velocity of 3 × 10^4 ms^{-1}.
   (b) Calculate the number of xenon ions ejected per second to produce a thrust of 0.5 N.
   (c) Explain why hydrogen ions (protons) ejected at the same speed as the xenon ions would produce less thrust.

5. A firefighter uses a high pressure hose to extinguish a fire.
    (a) Explain why they need to exert a force to prevent being pushed backward.

    The hose ejects 50 kg of water horizontally every second. The water leaves the end of the hose with a velocity of 4 ms⁻¹ and when it hits a nearby wall its velocity is reduced to zero and it does not rebound.
    (b) Calculate the force the water exerts on the wall.

6. Two trolleys A and B have masses m and 3m respectively. They are sitting on a horizontal track. They are joined together by a sprung clip. You may ignore friction between the trolleys and the tracks and at the wheels of the trolleys.

    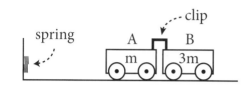

    The clip holding the trolleys together is released and the trolleys fly part. Trolley B moves to the right with velocity u.
    (a) Determine the velocity and direction of trolley A.

    Trolley A collides with a spring and rebounds without any loss of energy. Eventually trolley A catches up with and sticks to trolley B, both moving off with a common velocity v.
    (b) Calculate this common velocity in terms of u.
    (c) Initially, before the clip was released, the total momentum of the system was zero. Your answer to part (b) should reveal that the total momentum is no longer zero. Explain this result in terms of the Principle of Conservation of Momentum.

7. A tennis player hits a ball which reaches her with a velocity of 25 ms⁻¹. The maximum force she can hit the ball with is 250 N. The ball has a mass of 60 g. How long must the ball be in contact with the racket in order for the player to return the ball towards the other player with a velocity of 35 ms⁻¹?

8. Two cars approaching each other in a straight line collide. After the collision the two cars become stuck together. The masses of the two cars are shown on the diagram, along with their velocities just before they collide. Calculate:
    (a) The velocity of the two cars after the collision.
    (b) The direction in which move.
    (c) The kinetic energy lost in the collision.

    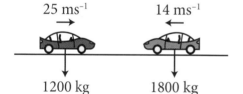

9. An object of mass m has a velocity v.
    (a) Write down an expression for its kinetic energy E_k and its momentum p.
    (b) Derive the relationship between E_k and p.

    Sphere A has a mass of 5 kg and is moving with velocity of 4 ms⁻¹. It collides with sphere B moving in the opposite direction. Sphere B has twice the momentum of sphere A. After the collision they stick together and move with a common velocity. Their total kinetic energy after the collision is 20 J.
    (c) Calculate the common velocity of the two spheres after the collision and state the direction in which they are moving.

10. A rifle is fired on a laboratory test. The rifle is found to recoil a distance of 3 cm in 15 ms. The mass of the bullet fired is 30 g. The mass of the rifle is 4.5 kg. Calculate the velocity of the bullet fired by the rifle.

11. A golf ball of mass 44 g is hit by a golf club. The graph opposite shows how the force acting on the ball varies with time. Use the graph and the information above to calculate the velocity of the ball just after it is no longer in contact with the head of the golf club.

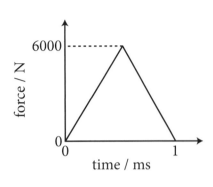

12. Two objects collide as shown opposite. After the collision the 5 kg object continues to move to the right with a velocity of 1.1 ms⁻¹.

    (a) Calculate the velocity of the 1 kg object after the collision and state the direction in which it is moving.
    (b) By performing the necessary calculations decide whether the collision is elastic or inelastic.

Unit 1.8 (AS 1)
Work done, potential and kinetic energy

1. The diagram shows part of the roller coaster in a fairground. The car is released from rest at O. It then accelerates down the slope.

   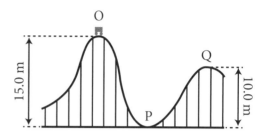

   (a) Determine the speed of the car at the point P assuming it loses 10% of its energy due to friction.
   (b) Determine the speed of the car at Q assuming it loses 10% of the energy it possessed at P.

2. The power P being supplied to a body by a constant force F, acting on it in the direction of its velocity v is given by the equation:

   $$P = Fv$$

   (a) Show that the base units on each side of the equation are consistent.

   A crane raises a load of 1000 kg from rest with a constant acceleration of 0.04g, where g is the acceleration of free-fall.
   (b) As this load moves upwards why is the power supplied to the load not constant?
   (c) Sketch a graph to show how the power supplied to the load changes with time as it moves from the ground to reach a height of 50 m. Your graph should show appropriate values of time and power.

3. A pile driver of mass 50 kg falls freely from a height of 10 m onto a vertical post of mass 200 kg. As the post is being driven into the ground there is an upward resistive force of 8 kN. Calculate how far into the ground the post is driven.

   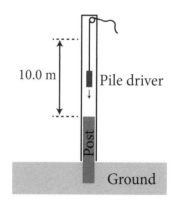

4. A car is raised on a hoist which is powered by an electric motor. The car has a mass of 1500 kg.

   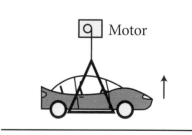

   The car is raised 200 cm in 8 s by the hoist.
   (a) Calculate the gravitational potential gained by the car.

   The electric motor has a power rating of 6 kW.
   (b) Calculate the efficiency of the hoist.
   (c) Calculate the friction forces resisting the motion of the car.

5. A block of wood slides down a frictionless curved track as shown in the diagram. The block mas mass M and it is released from a vertical height H.
    (a) Derive an expression for the velocity, v, of the block when it reaches the bottom of the track.
    (b) To find the velocity a student uses the equation $v^2 = u^2 + 2gH$. Explain why this is incorrect Physics.

6. A toy gun fires corks. The spring in the gun is compressed 5 cm by an average force of 0.75 N.
    (a) Calculate the work done in compressing the spring.

    When fired, 80% of the stored energy is converted to kinetic energy of the cork.
    (b) The cork has a mass of 3 g. Calculate the initial velocity of the cork when the gun is fired.

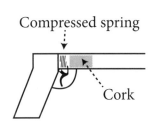
Compressed spring

Cork

7. A barrel of mass 50 kg rolls down a slope before falling over a cliff into the sea below. The vertical height of the cliff is 40 m. When it enters the water it has a velocity of 40 ms⁻¹. Calculate its kinetic energy and velocity at the point X, just as it falls over the edge of the cliff.

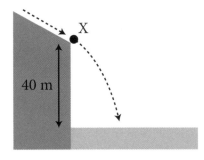
40 m

8. A pile driver of mass 150 kg fall from a height of 10 m. Energy losses amount to 20% of the initial potential energy of the pile driver. As it is being driven into the ground it is opposed by a constant force of 8500 N. Calculate how far the pile is driven into the ground.

9. The diagram shows a box on a frictionless surface. The box is already moving to the left. Three forces act on the box as shown. The forces act on the box over a horizontal distance of 2.0 m.
    (a) Calculate the work done on the box by the three forces.
    (b) Is the kinetic energy of the box increasing or decreasing? Explain your answer.

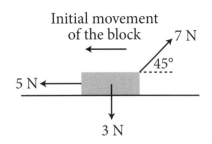
Initial movement of the block

7 N
45°
5 N
3 N

10. A pendulum is released from rest at the position shown. The length of the string attached to the pendulum is L. Derive an expression for the velocity of the pendulum bob when it reaches the lowest point of the swing.

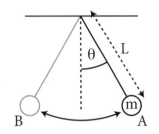
θ   L
m
B   A

11. The Highway Code gives the braking distance of a car travelling at 100 km per hour as 55 m.
    The mass of the car is 1750 kg.
    Using energy and work only calculate the braking force of this car.

12. Every second 50×10^3 kg of water fall onto a water wheel. The output
    power of the water wheel is 8×10^4 W and its efficiency is 0.2 (20%).
    Calculate the velocity of the water as it falls onto the water wheel.

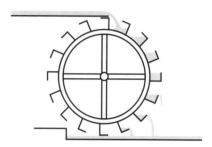

Unit 1.9 (AS 1)
Electric current and charge, potential difference and electromotive force

1. An electric charge of 1 coulomb passes a point in a circuit in 200 ms.
   (a) Calculate the electric current flowing in the circuit.
   (b) How many electrons have passed this point in the circuit?
   (c) What are the base units of the coulomb?

2. 3.0×10^{16} electrons pass a point in a circuit in 90 s.
   Calculate the current, in μA, flowing in this circuit.

3. An electric charge of 25 C passes through a 10 Ω in 20 s.
   (a) Calculate the current through the resistor.
   (b) How many electrons pass through the resistor in 1 s?

4. The very large number of collisions that electrons experience in a current carrying conductor means that their velocity through the conductor is very slow. For a current of 1 A in the wires normally found in a school laboratory, the velocity of the electrons is a fraction of 1 mm s^{-1}. This slow velocity is known as a drift velocity, v, and can be calculated using the equation below:

   $$I = nAve$$

   where:
   I is the current in amperes
   n is the number of electrons per m^3
   A is the cross-sectional area of the wire
   e is the charge on the electrons.

   Show that the base units on both sides of this equation are the same.

5. (a) Calculate the current, in amperes in the following cases:
      (i) A charge of 50 μC passes a point in 1 ms.
      (ii) A charge of 100 nC passes a point in 10 ps.

   (b) Calculate the charge, in coulombs, that passes in the following cases;
      (i) 5A flowing for 5 minutes.
      (ii) 1 mA flowing 10 μs.

6. The picture on a video display consists of a beam of electrons.
   The beam of electrons is equivalent to a current of 200 μA.
   How many electrons strike the screen each second?

7. A battery has an e.m.f. of 9 V. Calculate how much energy is converted into electrical energy when the following charge passes through it.
    (a) 5 C
    (b) 2 μC
    (c) 100 nC
    (d) A current of 200 mA for 1 s

8. A current of 100 mA passes through a resistor for 20 seconds.
    1.2 J of energy are transferred through the resistor in this time.
    Calculate the potential difference across the resistor.

9. Explain the difference between electromotive force and potential difference.

10. A battery of e.m.f. 9.0 V is connected to a bulb marked 9 V, 6 W. Using the definitions of electrical power and e.m.f calculate the energy when the bulb is switched on for 15 minutes.

11. An ideal battery has an e.m.f. of 12.0 V.
    (a) How much work does it do on an electron that passes through the battery from the positive to the negative terminal?
    (b) How much power is dissipated by the battery when 4.0×10^{18} electrons pass through the battery every second?

12. A battery has an e.m.f. of 9.0 V. It is marked 20 Ah, meaning it can deliver 20 amps for 1 hour or 1 amp for 20 hours. Assuming that the potential difference across the terminals remains constant, for how many hours can it deliver energy at the rate of 12 W?

Unit 1.10 (AS 1)
Resistance and resistivity

1. A resistance network is formed by connecting twelve equal length wires of resistance 6 Ω as the edges of a cube as shown. A current of 3 A enters at S and flows through the network leaving at Z.
    (a) Find the magnitude of the current in each wire.

    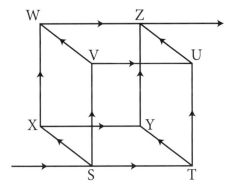

    The potential difference between S and Z may be calculated as the algebraic sum of the potential differences along any path from S to Z, such as S to V, V to U and U to Z. Remember each wire has a resistance of 6 Ω.
    (b) Using this information show that the resistance of the network between S and Z is 5 Ω.

2. (a) State the SI unit for electrical resistivity.
    (b) Derive the base units for electrical resistivity.

3. Two metal wires of identical length and area of cross-section are made of materials of resistivities ρ_1 and ρ_2. ρ_1 is greater than ρ_2. The two wires are connected in turn to a battery of negligible internal resistance.

    Use the expression for power, $P = \dfrac{V^2}{R}$ to derive expressions that will allow you to predict which wire will produce the greater heating effect.

4. A 12 V battery is connected to an arrangement of three bulbs as shown. Treating each bulb as a resistor of value 30 Ω, calculate the power dissipated in the bulbs.

    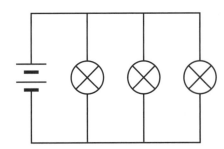

5. Materials can be classified a conductors, insulators and semiconductors. Give an example of each and state the approximate resistivity of each.

6. The filament of a bulb is 44 cm long and is made of tungsten wire of diameter 0.26 mm. The resistivity of tungsten is 5.4×10^{-6} Ωm at room temperature. Calculate the resistance of the filament before the lamp is switched on.

7. Calculate the total resistance of the circuit shown in the diagram.

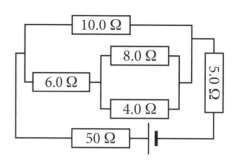

8. A network of resistors in shown opposite.
   Calculate the resistance between the following points:
   (a) AB
   (b) BC
   (c) CD
   (d) DA
   (e) BD
   (f) AC

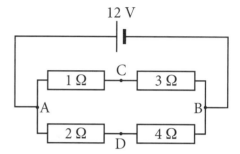

9. Look at the circuit opposite. Calculate the resistance of the circuit shown between the points A and B.

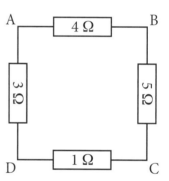

10. An electricity transmission cable consists of a central strand of steel surrounded by 6 strands of aluminium. The diameter of each of the strands is 5 mm.

    $$\rho_{steel} = 46 \times 10^{-8} \ \Omega m$$

    $$\rho_{aluminium} = 2.65 \times 10^{-8} \ \Omega m$$

    Calculate the resistance per kilometre of the cable.

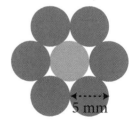

11. What is the resistance of a 3.0 m length of copper wire of diameter 1.2 mm?
    The resistivity of copper is $1.68 \times 10^{-8} \ \Omega m$.

12. What is the diameter of a 0.8 m length of tungsten wire of resistance 0.35 Ω?
    The resistivity of tungsten is $5.62 \times 10^{-8} \ \Omega m$.

Unit 1.11 (AS 1)
Internal resistance and electromotive force

1. A cell in a small torch has an e.m.f. of 1.55 V and an internal resistance of 0.8 Ω.
   The bulb to which it is connected has a resistance of 5.2 Ω when hot.
   Calculate the following:
   (a) The current drawn by the bulb when it is lit.
   (b) The potential difference across the bulb.
   (c) The power dissipated within the cell.

2. The circuit shown below was set up and values of current and voltage were recorded. The values are then plotted on the graph shown. Using the graph determine the e.m.f of the cell and its internal resistance.

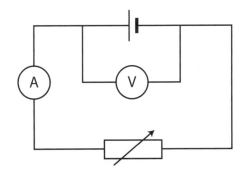
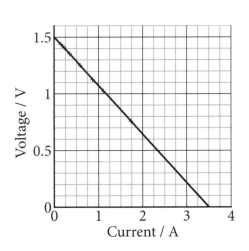

3. A battery of e.m.f. 12.0 V shows a terminal potential difference of 11.8 V when connected across a resistor of value 10 Ω. Calculate the internal resistance of the battery.

4. A battery has e.m.f. 6.00 V and internal resistance 0.500 Ω. Calculate the terminal potential difference when it is connected in series with:
   (a) a resistor of value 5.0 Ω,
   (b) a resistor of value 500 Ω.

5. Eight 1.5 V cells are connected in series to form a 12 V battery. When connected to a 12 Ω resistor the current that flows is 0.6 A. Calculate the internal resistance of each cell.

6. A car battery of e.m.f. 12.0 V is used to start a car. When it is connected to the starter motor, a current of 60 A is drawn from the battery and the terminal potential difference of the battery drops to 9.0 V. Calculate the internal resistance of the battery.

7. A battery with an internal resistance is connected to a circuit. When a current of 1.0 A is drawn from the battery the terminal potential is measured as 5.7 V. When the current is increased to 2.0 A the terminal potential difference is measured as 5.4 V. Calculate the e.m.f. and internal resistance of the battery.

8. When a 6.0 Ω resistor is connected across the terminals of a battery a current of 1.0 A flows through the resistor. When the 6.0 Ω resistor is replaced by a 3.0 Ω resistor a current of 1.5 A flows. Calculate the e.m.f and internal resistance of the cell.

9. When a voltmeter of resistance 8 kΩ is connected across the terminals of a power supply known to have an e.m.f. of 2000 V, the reading is found to be only 1950 V. Calculate the internal resistance of the power supply.

10. A voltmeter with a resistance of 10 kΩ is connected across a power supply it gives a reading of 32.0 V. When a voltmeter of resistance of 20 kΩ is connected across the same power supply it gives a reading of 33.9 V. Calculate the e.m.f. of the power supply.

11. A battery of e.m.f. 9.0 V and internal resistance 1.5 Ω is connected across a filament bulb of resistance 12.0 Ω. Calculate;
    (a) the current supplied by the battery,
    (b) the power consumption by the bulb,
    (c) the power consumed by the internal resistance of the battery.

12. A battery of e.m.f. 6.0 V and internal resistance 0.5 Ω is connected in series with a 2.0 Ω resistor. Calculate the value of the resistor that must be connected in parallel with the 2.0 Ω so that the potential difference across the internal resistance is 3.0 V.

Unit 1.12 (AS 1)
Potential dividers

1. Two resistors of 40 kΩ and 10 kΩ are connected in series with a 10 V battery of negligible internal resistance.
   (a) What is the potential difference across each resistor?
   (b) A voltmeter of resistance 10 kΩ is then connected across the 10 kΩ resistor. What voltage does the meter indicate?
   (c) Find the current drawn by the voltmeter when it is connected across the 10 kΩ resistor.

2. A sealed 12 V battery is to provide an output voltage which may be varied between a minimum of 3 V and a maximum of 9 V.
   (a) Draw a labelled circuit diagram to show how such a variable voltage could be obtained. On your diagram clearly indicate where the 12 V battery is connected and where the output voltage is obtained.
   (b) Calculate values for the components used in the circuit.

3. The circuit diagram shows a simple design for a 'movement' sensor used in an earthquake region. The supply has negligible internal resistance.

   The resistance wire is stretched between two rigid steel plates, not shown in the diagram. During an earthquake, ground movement changes the separation between the plates and so the length of wire changes. The wire has an area of cross section of 1.2 mm² and length 32 cm. It is made of a material of resistivity 6.8×10^{-6} Ωm.
   (a) Show that the resistance of the wire is 1.8 Ω.
   (b) Calculate the potential difference between A and B.
   (c) The length of the wire increases. State and explain the effect on the p.d. between A and B.

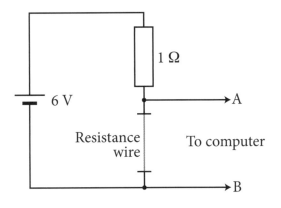

4. The potential divider circuit shown opposite was set up.
   (a) Calculate the potential difference between A and B.
   (b) A bulb marked 4 V, 0.2 A is now connected between A and B. How will its brightness appear? Explain your answer.
   (c) It is proposed to replace the 200 Ω resistor with one of 0.5 Ω and the 400 Ω resistor with one of 1.0 Ω. Draw the circuit diagram for this. What effect does it have on the brightness of the bulb? Support your answer with a suitable calculations.

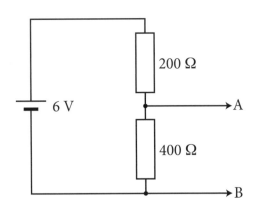

5. The potential divider circuit contains a light dependent resistor (LDR). The resistance of the LDR in darkness is 500 kΩ and in bright light is 1000 Ω.
    (a) Calculate the value of V_R and V_{LDR} in darkness and in bright light.
    (b) Calculate the current flowing in the circuit in darkness and in bright light.

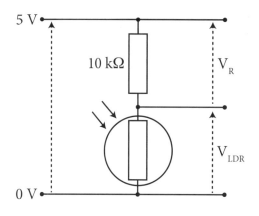

6. The potential divider circuit contains a thermistor. The thermistor has a resistance of 1000 Ω at 0°C. Over a limited temperature range the change in resistance ΔR is related to the change in temperature ΔT by the equation:
    $$\Delta R = -16\Delta T$$
    What is the temperature when the output voltage is 4.0 V?

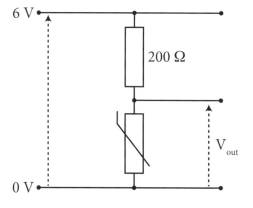

7. Determine the range of output voltages between A and B for the potential divider circuit shown.

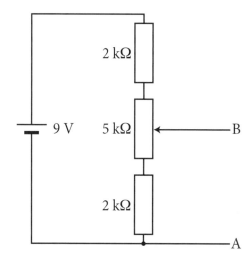

8. A 50 cm length of resistance wire XY is connected across a 9 V battery as shown in the diagram. A 4 V battery is connected to a sensitive ammeter as shown. At what distance from the end X should the moveable contact be placed so that no current flows in the ammeter?

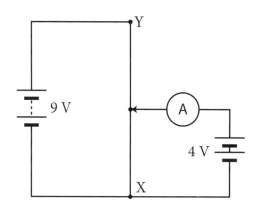

9. The potential divider shown opposite was set up.
   (a) What should the value of variable resistor R_1 if V_{out} is to equal 2 V ?
   (b) A voltmeter of resistance 1 kΩ is then connected across the 3 kΩ, what reading would it show ?

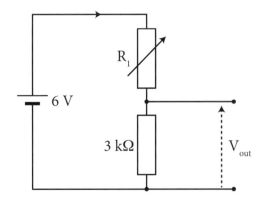

10. A potential divider circuit is created using 50 V as the input voltage. A load resistor R_{load} is connected as shown. Calculate the potential difference across the load when:
    (a) R_{load} = 47 kΩ
    (b) R_{load} = 4.7 kΩ

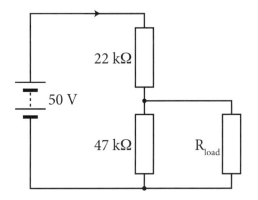

11. The circuit shown opposite contains a 12 V battery and a network of resistors with a voltmeter connected between X and Y.
    (a) What is reading on the voltmeter when R has a value of 2 kΩ, which point X or Y is at the higher potential?
    (b) What value of R will produce a reading of zero on the voltmeter?

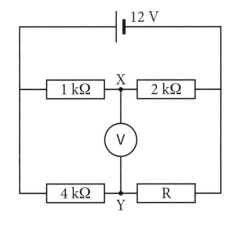

12. A bulb marked 3.0 V, 6 W is to be used with a 6 V supply. A student set up the circuit shown. To allow the bulb to operate at normal brightness suggest values for the resistors R_1 and R_2. Choose your resistors from the following:
    • R_1 and R_2 = 20 Ω
    • R_1 and R_2 = 10 Ω
    • R_1 and R_2 = 0.5 Ω

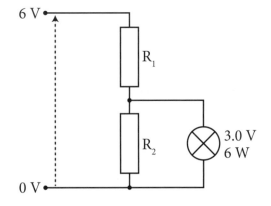

Unit 2.1 (AS 2)
Waves

1. Explain the difference between transverse and longitudinal waves and give an example of each.

2. The speed of electromagnetic waves is 3×10^8 ms^{-1}.
   Calculate:
   (a) the frequency of yellow light of wavelength 600 nm;
   (b) the wavelength of microwaves of frequency 1.5×10^{10} Hz.

3. A sound wave has a frequency of 500 Hz and a wavelength of 0.68 m.
   Calculate:
   (a) the speed of this sound wave;
   (b) the wavelength of a sound wave which has the same speed, but a frequency of 680 Hz.

4. The speed of the transverse waves in a stretched wire is directly proportional to the square root of the tension in the wire. A particular wave has a speed of 50 ms^{-1} when the tension is 36 N.
   Calculate:
   (a) the *increase* in tension required to raise the speed to 100 ms^{-1};
   (b) the speed of the waves when the tension in the wire is 9 N.

5. The period of a water wave is 5 s.
   The horizontal distance between the first and seventh peaks is 63 cm.
   Calculate:
   (a) the frequency of the waves;
   (b) the wavelength of the waves;
   (c) the speed of the waves.

6. A water wave has amplitude 12 cm and a wavelength of 30 cm.
   Calculate:
   (a) (i) the maximum and
       (ii) the minimum vertical distance between two points which are out of phase by 180°.
   (b) the horizontal distance between two points within the same wavelength which have a phase difference of 90°.

7. What is the phase difference between two waves, each of wavelength 24 cm, when one leads the other by
   (a) 6 cm
   (b) 8 cm
   (c) 12 cm?

8. Two waves travel in water. Each wave has a speed of 24 ms^{-1}.
   Calculate the difference in the frequencies of the waves if their wavelengths are 6 cm and 8 cm.

9. Explain what is meant by "polarised light".

10. Sound waves cannot be polarised. Explain why not.

11. A wave of amplitude 4 cm and frequency 5 Hz travels along a stretched wire at speed of 10 ms^{-1}. Calculate:
    (a) the period and sketch a graph of displacement against time to represent the wave, showing two complete cycles;
    (b) the wavelength and sketch a graph of displacement against distance to represent the wave, showing two complete cycles;
    (c) the phase difference between two points on the wire which are:
        (i) 0.8 m apart, and
        (ii) 2.8 m apart, giving your answer in degrees.

12. The shortest distance between two points on a progressive wave having a phase difference of 60° is 5 cm. The frequency of the wave is 50 Hz.
    Calculate the wave speed.

Unit 2.2 (AS 2)
Refraction

1. When light is incident on a transparent material it may be refracted.
   (a) State Snell's Law of Refraction.
   (b) What is meant by the refractive index of a transparent material?
   (c) In what unit is refractive index measured?

2. Light of wavelength 600 nm in air falls incident on a glass block of refractive index 1.50. The light is refracted.
   (a) Calculate the wavelength, frequency and speed of the light in the glass.
   (b) If the angle of refraction in the glass is 30°, calculate the angle of incidence in the air.

3. A ray of monochromatic light falls incident on an equilateral triangular glass prism of refractive index 1.50. The angle of incidence is 45°.
   Calculate the angle between the ray that eventually re-emerges back into the air and the prism.

4. The refractive index of a particular glass is 1.52 for yellow light. When an experiment is carried out using red light, it is found that the glass has a different refractive index. Explain this phenomenon and state whether the refractive index increases or decreases with increasing wavelength.
   (Hint: Recall what happens when a glass prism disperses white light.)

5. A right-angled isosceles prism is made of glass of refractive index 1.50. A ray of light strikes the longer face of the prism normally, as shown in the diagram, so that the angle of incidence is 0°.
   Calculate the angle between the ray that re-emerges into the air and the normal to the surface. Illustrate your answer with a diagram.

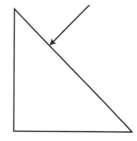

6. Describe, in detail, how you could verify Snell's Law and measure the refractive index of glass using a rectangular glass block. In your description you should:
   (i) draw a labelled diagram of the apparatus you intend to use.
   (ii) describe how the apparatus is used to obtain measurements.
   (iii) explain how the measurements are used to verify Snell's Law.

7. A student traces the path of a narrow beam of light through a transparent plastic block, and measures the angles θ_a and θ_p (see diagram).
   (a) Explain why there is no refraction **at the curved surface** of the semicircular plastic block.

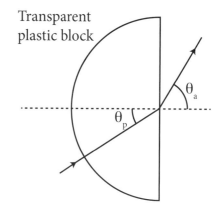

Transparent plastic block

She repeats the measurements for various chosen values of θ_p. Her results are shown in the table below.

θ_p / °	10	20	30	40	45
θ_a / °	14	29	43	64	82

(b) Plot the graph of θ_a / ° (vertical axis) against θ_p / ° (horizontal axis).
(c) Using **only** your graph, and without calculation, estimate the critical angle of the plastic.
(d) Use your answer to (c) to calculate the refractive index of the plastic.

8. The step-index optical fibre shown in the diagram below has a core of refractive index 1.530. The maximum angle, θ, between a light path and the axis (see diagram), which still allows light to travel for a long distance through the fibre, is 7°.

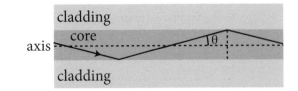

(a) Calculate the critical angle at the core-cladding boundary.
(b) Use your answer to part (a) to calculate the refractive index of the cladding with respect to air.
(c) Suggest why engineers seek to make the angle θ as small as possible.

9. An equilateral triangular glass prism is made of a material of refractive index 1.50. A ray of light is incident on one face of the prism is just totally internally reflected at the second face as shown in the diagram. Calculate the angle of incidence in the air.

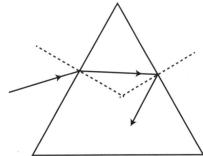

10. A ray of light is refracted at as it enters a glass block of refractive index 1.52. Copy and complete the table below to show the changes which occur.

Angle of incidence in air / °	Angle of refraction in glass / °	Speed of light in air / ms^{-1}	Speed of light in glass / ms^{-1}	Wavelength of light in air / nm	Wavelength of light in glass / nm
28				600	

In what way, if at all, does the frequency of the light change as it enters the glass?

11. The table shows the speed of ultrasound in soft tissue and bone.

Medium	Soft tissue	Bone
Speed of ultrasound / ms^{-1}	1500	4000

Calculate the angle of refraction in bone when a beam of ultrasound is incident at 10° on a soft tissue to bone boundary.

12. An optical fibre consists of a core and a cladding, both of which are made of glass. In a particular fibre the cladding has a refractive index of 1.47. Explain carefully why the refractive index of the core must be bigger than 1.47.

Unit 2.3 part 1 (AS 2)
Lenses

1. (a) Explain what is meant by
    - (i)   the principal focus and
    - (ii) the focal length of a converging lens.
    (b) Draw a large ray diagram to show how a converging lens can produce a real image of an object at infinity.

2. An object 5 cm tall is placed 6 cm in front of a converging lens of focal length 4 cm. By drawing a full scale ray diagram on graph paper, find:
    (a) the distance between the image and the object;
    (b) the magnification of the image;
    (c) the nature of the image.

3. A lens is used as a magnifying glass by a stamp collector. The upright image of the stamp is 12 cm from the lens and its linear magnification is 2. The image is a square of side 4 cm. Calculate:
    (a) the distance between the stamp and the lens;
    (b) the focal length of the lens;
    (c) the dimensions of the stamp.
    (d) State whether the image is real or virtual and give a reason for your answer.

4. When an object is placed 12 cm from a convex lens the image is the same height as the object. How far and in what direction must the object be moved to obtain:
    (a) a real image of magnification 2;
    (b) a virtual image of magnification 2.

5. The focal length of a camera lens is 50 mm. How far from the image must the lens be set in order to photograph an object 2.5 m from the lens?

6. Find:
    (a) the power of a converging lens of focal length 40 cm and
    (b) the focal length of a lens of power -4 D. What type of lens is that referred to in (b)?

7. Copy and complete the table below for a converging lens:

Position of Object	Position of Image	Nature of Image		
		Real/Virtual	Enlarged/Diminished	Upright/Inverted
	At ∞			
At ∞				
			Same size as object	
Between F and 2F				
	Between F and 2F			
		Virtual		

8. What type of lens gives a virtual, diminished and upright image of a real object?

9. A certain lens has a power of –5 D. An object 10 cm tall is placed 5 cm away from this lens.
    (a) Calculate the focal length of the lens.
    (b) Calculate the distance between the object and the image.
    (c) Calculate the magnification of the image.
    (d) Calculate the height of the image.
    (e) State the nature of this image.
    (f) Illustrate your answers with a ray diagram.

10. The diagram below shows a converging lens, its principal
    focus and a virtual image.
    (a) Copy the diagram and draw two rays to locate the
        position of the object.
    (b) Mark on the diagram where the eye should be
        positioned to view the image.

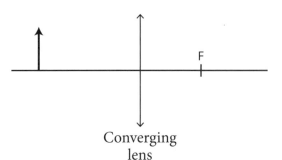

Converging lens

The object is now moved and the image becomes real.
    (c) In what direction:
        (i) is the object moved? (ii) does the image move?

11. An object placed 20 cm from a lens gives an image of magnification 4. Calculate the possible focal
    lengths of the lens.

12. An object O is placed a fixed distance D from a screen.
    When a converging lens is placed in position L_1 a sharp
    image is seen on the screen. The lens is moved towards
    the screen and the image is seen to become very blurred.
    When the lens is displaced by a distance d, and is now
    in position L_2, another sharp image is observed on the
    screen. It can be shown that the focal length of the lens, f
    is given by:

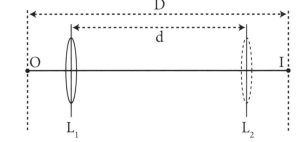

$$f = \frac{(D^2 - d^2)}{4D}$$

The experiment is then repeated for different distances, D, and the corresponding distances, d, are
measured. The results are shown in the table below.

D / m	1.00	1.20	1.40	1.60	1.80	2.00
d / m	0.63	0.85	1.06	1.26	1.47	1.67

    (a) In what way are the images found when the lens is in positions L_1 and L_2
        (i) similar? (ii) different?
    (b) What straight line graph could be drawn to find the focal length of the lens?
    (c) Copy the table and use the blank rows in the table to calculate the data needed to plot this graph. Be
        sure to label each row correctly.
    (d) Plot the graph and draw the line of best fit.
    (e) Calculate the gradient of your graph and give its unit.
    (f) What is your best estimate of the focal length of the lens?
    (g) At the minimum distance between the object and screen which still gives a real image, the distance
        d is zero. Find the minimum distance for this lens.

Unit 2.3 part 2 (AS 2)
Defects of vision

1. With the help of labelled diagrams describe and explain what is meant by:
    (a) short sight;
    (b) long sight.

2. A certain student requires spectacles in order to see a book clearly at normal reading distance.
    (a) What defect of vision do the spectacle lenses correct?
    (b) What is the normal cause of this defect?
    (c) Without spectacles, the student cannot see clearly objects which are nearer than 80 cm from the eye. Calculate the power of the spectacle lens required to reduce this distance to the normal near-point distance of 25 cm.
    (d) Without spectacles, the student's far-point distance has the normal value.
        (i) Calculate the distance of the student's far point from the eye when the spectacles in (c) are worn.
        (ii) When wearing the spectacles in (c), the student looks at a road sign which is 5 m away. Comment briefly on the appearance of the sign to the student.

3. The range of vision of a patient is 40 cm – 400 cm. If the student wears a lens of power –0.2 D, what is the range of vision now?

4. The lens of the human eye is said to be *unaccommodated* when viewing objects at an infinite distance. The lens of a normal unaccommodated eye has a power of +50 D. Calculate:
    (a) the distance between the lens and the retina;
    (b) the increase in power of the lens when it focuses on an object at the normal near point.

5. A physics student observes that his optician has prescribed a lens of power –0.04 D.
    (a) From what defect of vision does this student suffer?
    (b) At what distance is the student's far point?

    The student's girlfriend's prescription is for lenses of power +2.5D.
    (c) From what defect of vision does she suffer?
    (d) At what distance is her near point?

6. A child has an eye lens which is 2.0 cm from her retina. The power of her lens can be varied from 55 D to 60 D.
    (a) How far from her eye is her near point?
    (b) Can the child focus on objects at an infinite distance from her eye?
    (c) From what defect of the vision does the child suffer?

7. When a boy with normal vision focuses on a point 40 cm away, the lens of his eye has a power of 55 D. What is the power of the same eye lens when focused on a point 200 cm away?

8. A long sighted person can focus on an object no closer than 1.5 m away. Calculate the power of contact lens required to enable this eye to focus on an object 30 cm away.

9. A patient has a near point of 15 cm and a far point of 450 cm.
   (a) Is she long-sighted, short-sighted or both long-sighted and short-sighted? Give a reason for your answer.
   (b) What is the power of the contact lens you would prescribe to give her a near point of 25 cm?

10. A young person with a near point of 24 cm, is not able to see an object clearly if it is more than 5 m from his eye. What kind of lens should you prescribe to correct his vision?

11. The power, P, of the lens in a person's eye changes as they focus on objects at different distances, d, from their eye according to the equation:

$$P = \frac{1}{d} + k$$

The table below gives the power for different distances.

P / D	53.33	52.50	51.67	51.43	51.25	51.11	51.00
d / m	0.30	0.40	0.60	0.70	0.80	0.90	1.00

   (a) What graph would you plot to obtain a straight line graph from these data?
   (b) Copy the table and use the third row to obtain the data necessary to plot this graph.
   (c) Plot the graph and draw the line of best fit. Remember you do not need to start from a (0, 0) origin.
   (d) State the unit in which k must be measured.
   (e) Use the graph to find the value of k.
   (f) What is the power of the lens when the eye is unaccommodated, that is it is viewing objects at an infinite distance from the eye?
   (g) Calculate the distance between the eye lens and the retina from the data.

12. The distance between a girl's eye lens and her retina is 20 mm. She focuses on a picture measuring 45 cm by 30 cm at a distance of 60 cm from her eye. What are the dimensions of the image of the picture on her retina?

Unit 2.4 part 1 (AS 2)
Superposition

1. State the Principle of Superposition of Waves.

2. (a) In terms of energy, describe the difference between a stationary wave and a progressive wave.
    (b) What are the necessary conditions to produce a standing wave?

3. The graphs show two waves of different amplitudes and frequencies. Both waves have the same speed.
    (a) Calculate the ratio of their (i) amplitudes (ii) frequencies and (iii) wavelengths.
    (b) The waves superpose. Use the Principle of Superposition to sketch the resultant wave.
    (c) The frequency of the wave with the larger frequency is f. Calculate the frequency of the resultant wave.

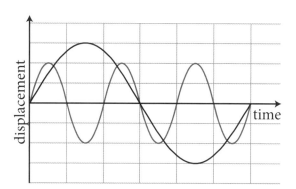

4. The data below shows how the speed of sound changes with temperature for a gas, H.

Speed of sound, v / ms⁻¹	269	278	287	296	304	312
Temperature, T / °C	20	40	60	80	100	120

Speed of sound, v / ms^{-1} — Temperature, T / °C

   (a) By drawing a suitable straight-line graph, show that these data are consistent with the hypothesis that the speed of sound is directly proportional to the square root of the *kelvin* temperature.
   (b) Use your graph to estimate the speed of sound in gas H at 0 °C.

5. A loudspeaker, connected to a signal generator, is placed close to the open end of a resonance tube closed at the opposite end. The frequency of the signal generator is increased until the first position of resonance is obtained.
    (a) How would the experimentalist know when resonance was taking place?
    (b) What two precautions would the experimentalist take to ensure that this is the *first* position of resonance?
    (c) (i) On a copy of the diagram shown, illustrate the mode of vibration at the *second* position of resonance, and label all nodes (N) and antinodes (A).

signal generator

   The tube is 30 cm long and the frequency of the note at the *second* position of resonance is 850 Hz.
   (ii) Calculate the wavelength of the standing wave in the tube at the second position of resonance.
   (iii) Use your answer to part (ii) to calculate the speed of the standing wave in the tube.

   The air in the tube is now replaced with gas, G, in which sound travels at 1020 ms⁻¹.
   (iv) What is the frequency of the sound at the second position of resonance when the tube is filled with gas, G?

6. The graph shows two different waves A and B.
    (a) Waves A and wave B superpose to produce wave C.
        Sketch wave C on the grid.
    (b) Calculate the frequencies of the three waves.
    (c) Calculate the phase difference between A and B.

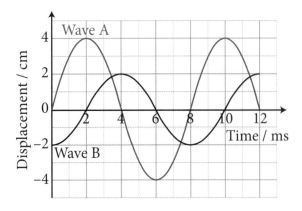

7. An experiment is carried out on standing waves using the apparatus shown in the diagram below. The distance between the vibration generator and the pulley, L, is 0.8 m.

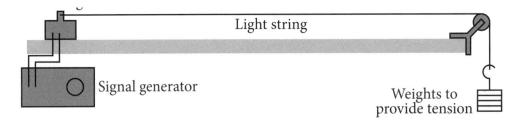

The frequencies, f_n, of the various modes of vibration, n, are measured and recorded as in the table below.

Mode of vibration, n	1	2	3	4	5	6
Frequency, f_n / Hz	28.1	56.3	84.4	112	141	169

n = 1 corresponds to the first (fundamental) mode,
n = 2 corresponds to the next highest mode and so on.

    (a) Show that the relationship between f_n and n is $f_n = \dfrac{nv}{2L}$, where v is the speed of the standing wave on the string.
    (b) Plot the graph of f_n against n and determine its gradient to 2 significant figures.
    (c) Use your answer to (b) to find the speed of the standing waves on the string to 2 significant figures.

8. A student finds the difference in the tube lengths at the first and second positions of resonance is 33.2 cm when using a tuning fork of frequency 512 Hz. Use this information to find the speed of sound.

9. The resonant cavity of a semiconductor laser has reflecting ends a distance 0.215 mm apart. Within this cavity standing waves may be set up, with a node at each end of the cavity.
    (a) Explain what is meant by a node in a standing wave.
    (b) Show that while it is possible to have standing wave of wavelength 860.0 nm within this cavity, it is not possible to have a standing wave of wavelength 865 nm.

10. A vibration generator produces standing waves of frequency 50 Hz and speed 45 ms^{-1} in a stretched wire. What length of wire will show a standing wave pattern with exactly 3 antinodes?

11. The diagram shows a microwave transmitter and a reflector placed about a metre apart. Microwaves are emitted continuously by the transmitter and reflected continuously by the reflector. As the receiver moves between the transmitter and reflector it detects points where the microwave intensity is zero and other points where the intensity is a maximum.

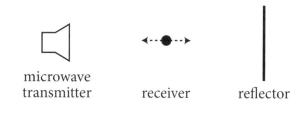

microwave transmitter   receiver   reflector

    (a) Explain this phenomenon.
    (b) The distance between the 1ˢᵗ and 7ᵗʰ successive points of maximum intensity is 9 cm. Calculate the wavelength and frequency of the microwaves.

12. In a book on Advanced Physics Chris reads that the position of the antinode in a resonance tube closed at one end is not exactly at the end of the tube. The book goes on to say that at fundamental resonance the length, L, of the tube is related to the wavelength, λ, by the equation:

$$L = \frac{\lambda}{4} - e$$

    Chris carries out an experiment to find the value of the constant e by measuring the length L for different frequencies at fundamental resonance. He obtains the following results.

Frequency f/Hz	250	300	350	400	450	500
Length L/cm	32.0	26.3	22.3	19.3	16.9	15.0
$\frac{1}{f}$ / Hz^{-1}						

    (a) Obtain an expression for the wavelength of the standing wave in terms of L and e.
    (b) Hence show that $L = \frac{v}{4f} - e$ where v is the speed of the standing waves in the tube.
    (c) Using the data in the table, plot a suitable straight line graph from which it is possible to find the values of v and e.
    (d) From your graph, find the values of v and e.

Unit 2.4 part 2 (AS 2)
Interference

1. In a Young's double slit experiment using violet light of wavelength 400 nm the separation of adjacent fringes is 600 μm. The violet lamp is replaced by one emitting light yellow light of wavelength 550 nm. The remainder of the apparatus is unchanged. By how much is the separation of adjacent fringes changed as a result?

2. Monochromatic light illuminates a narrow slit which is 8000 mm from a white screen. Two narrow parallel slits, 600 μm apart are placed midway between the single slit and the screen. The separation of the interference fringes on the screen is 4.0 mm. Calculate the wavelength of the light.

3. When sunlight is used with Young's slits apparatus the central fringe is white, but tinged with red at the extreme ends of the fringe. Explain this phenomenon.

4. Two loudspeakers S_1 and S_2 are connected to a signal generator and produce coherent waves of frequency 1650 Hz that are in phase.
    (a) Explain what is meant by coherent.
    (b) Explain what is meant by the sound waves at S_1 and S_2 being "in phase". Express your answer in terms of wave compressions.

    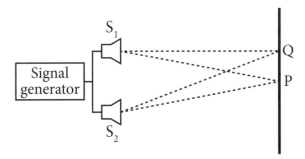

    A microphone at point P (on the axis of symmetry) detects a sound intensity maximum. As the microphone moves from P towards Q the detected sound intensity decreases continuously, until at Q no sound is detected at all.
    (c) What is the phase difference between the waves at Q coming from S_1 and those coming from S_2?
    (d) If the speed of sound in air is 330 ms⁻¹, calculate the path difference ($S_2Q - S_1Q$) between the interfering waves at Q.

5. The double slit shown in the diagram is illuminated with monochromatic light of wavelength 600 nm in such a way that S_1 and S_2 behave as coherent sources with a constant phase difference, φ. S_1 and S_2 are 500 μm apart and the distance from the screen is 4.0 m. At point C on the axis of symmetry there is a dark fringe. The nearest bright fringe to C occurs at point P.

    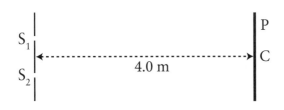

    (a) State the value of φ in degrees.
    (b) Calculate the distance CP.

6. A student uses a beam of monochromatic light to obtain fringes using Young's double slits. She then measures the distance, y, from the central fringe to the middle of adjacent fringes of order n, and obtains the following results:

Distance, y / mm	0	2.9	6.1	8.9	12.1	14.9	18.1
Order, n	0	1	2	3	4	5	6

   (a) Plot the graph of y against n and find its gradient.
   (b) Given that the distance between the slits and the screen is 5000 times the separation of the slits themselves, use your answer to (a) to calculate the wavelength of the light used.

7. Two loudspeakers S_1 and S_2 are connected to a signal generator and produce coherent waves of frequency 1700 Hz. A microphone at point P (on the axis of symmetry) detects a sound intensity **minimum**. As the microphone moves from P towards Q the detected sound intensity increases continuously, until at Q it is a **maximum**.

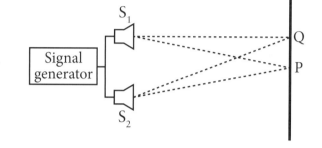

   (a) By considering the phase difference of the sound coming from the loudspeakers, give a possible reason why the intensity is a minimum at P and a maximum at Q.
   (b) Given that the distance PQ is 0.25 m, the separation of the speakers is 0.5 m and the speakers are 1.25 m away from the line of detection, calculate the wavelength and speed of the sound.
   (c) Describe how, if at all, the distance between adjacent maxima on the line of detection would change, if the control on the signal generator were adjusted to obtain sound of higher frequency from the loudspeakers.

8. Two waves of amplitude 2 cm and 1 cm interfere destructively, with the peak of one wave coinciding with the trough of the other. At the point of destructive interference the resultant intensity is I.
   (a) Use the Principle of Superposition to find the amplitude, A, of the resultant disturbance at the point of destructive interference.
   (b) Given that the intensity is directly proportional to the square of the amplitude of the resultant disturbance, write down an equation showing the relationship between A and I. Give the meaning of any other symbol used in your equation.
   (c) In terms of I, find the intensity at a point where the same two waves interfere constructively, with the crest of one coinciding with the crest of the other.

9. A double slit is illuminated with light from a laser pointer emitting red light and the resultant interference pattern is observed on a white screen. What two differences would be observed on the screen if the same double slit were illuminated with green laser light? The distance between the slits and the screen is unchanged.

10. When observing a Young's interference pattern obtained using monochromatic light from a sodium lamp, it is a good idea to pull the window blinds to darken the room. When observing a Young's interference pattern obtained using laser light, it is a **not** a good idea to darken the room completely. Explain why this is so.

11. A technician is asked to set up the apparatus needed to demonstrate Young's Double Slit Interference experiment. The teacher has said that she wishes the centres of the bright fringes to be at least 4 mm apart on the screen. The laser can be up to 5 m from the screen. Two lasers are available, one gives light of wavelength 630 nm and the other at 511 nm. The technician is asked to make the double slit, but the equipment available only allows him to prepare slits of 0.7 mm separation or more.
    (a) Which laser should the technician use?
    (b) What is the maximum separation of the slits to produce the required pattern?

12. In an interference experiment using a double slit of separation 0.95 mm, fringes are observed using a travelling microscope. The distance between the double slit and the fringes is 80.0 cm. The distance between the centres of the first and the twenty-first dark fringe is 9.00 mm. Calculate the wavelength of the light used.

1. The diagram and graphs shown illustrate the diffraction pattern produced when a narrow slit is illuminated with green laser light.

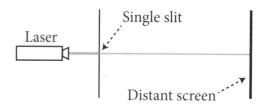

On a copy of the grid in the diagram below, sketch the Intensity-position graph you would expect if the slit had been slightly larger when using the green laser. The apparatus is otherwise identical.

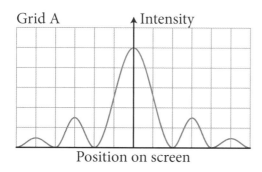

2. A diffraction grating is marked "300 lines / mm".
    (a) Calculate the width of the grating element (slit width). Give your answer in nm.
    (b) How does the width of the slit compare with the wavelength of visible light?

3. A diffraction grating ruled with 300 lines per millimetre is illuminated normally with light of wavelength 600 nm.
    (a) Calculate the highest order diffraction that will be observed.
    (b) How many lines will be observed in the diffraction pattern?

4. A diffraction grating has 600 lines/mm. It is illuminated by a laser light of wavelength 532 nm.
    (a) Calculate the angle between the two first order diffracted beams.
    (b) How many laser spots are seen on a screen placed near the diffraction grating?

5. In an experiment to measure the number of lines per mm on a diffraction grating the following measurements were recorded.

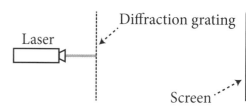

>   *Wavelength of the laser light = 473 nm*
>
>   *Distance from diffraction grating to screen = 0.75 m*
>
>   *Distance between the **two** 1st order diffracted images = 28.8 cm*

Calculate the number of lines per mm of the diffraction grating used.

6. The element sodium emits two yellow lines with very similar wavelengths. These are known as the sodium D-lines and they have wavelengths 589.0 nm and 589.6 nm. A diffraction grating as 1200 lines/mm. Calculate the angular separation in the first order diffracted beams of these two wavelengths.

7. A beam light containing two wavelengths 450 nm and 675 nm is passed through a diffraction grating. The diffraction grating has 300 lines/mm. Certain orders of diffraction of the 450 nm light coincide with certain orders of diffraction of the 650 nm light. Determine the lowest non-zero order for each wavelength for which this coincidence occurs.

8. A diffraction grating is made of a number of fine wires, each of diameter 10 μm with spaces of width 7.5 μm between them. A beam of electromagnetic radiation of wavelength 3 μm is incident normally on the grating.
    (a) To what region of the electromagnetic spectrum does this radiation belong?
    (b) Calculate the width of the grating element, d.
    (c) Calculate the angular separation of the second order maxima in the diffraction pattern.

9. Monochromatic light of wavelength 600 nm falls incident on a diffraction grating. The angle of diffraction, θ, is measured for the different orders. The results are recorded in the table below.

Angle of diffraction, θ / °	8.60	17.5	26.7	36.9	48.6	64.2
Order	1	2	3	4	5	6

   (a) Plot a suitable straight line graph from which the width of the grating element, d, could be found. You will need to complete the last row in the table.
   (b) Determine the gradient of your graph.
   (c) State the unit, if any, in which the gradient is measured.
   (d) Use your answer to part (b) to find the grating element, d.
   (e) Use your graph to find the highest order of diffraction possible when this grating is illuminated with light of wavelength 600 nm.

10. A laser beam is shone normally at a diffraction grating with 500 lines per millimetre. The angle of diffraction of the **second** order beams is 39.3°.
    (a) Calculate the wavelength of the laser light.
    (b) Calculate the angle of diffraction of the **third** order beams
    (c) The beams of different orders are spaced much further apart than the fringes in a typical Young's slits set-up using the same laser. Why is this so?

11. A diffraction grating is 25 mm square and contains 10 000 lines. When it is illuminated with monochromatic light the angle of diffraction in the first order is 14.7°. Calculate the wavelength of the light used.

12. When light from a neighbouring star (Alpha Centauri) was passed through a diffraction grating, four bright lines in the second order were found corresponding to wavelengths 656 nm, 486 nm, 434 nm and 410 nm. No higher orders could be observed with the grating used. What is the smallest diffraction element, d, which could show these lines?

Unit 2.5 (AS 2)
Quantum physics

1. (a) Light is said to be "quantised". What does this mean?
   (b) Find the energy possessed by a quantum of light of wavelength 600 nm.

2. Copy and complete the table below for a quantum of radiation of frequency 1×10^{15} Hz.

Speed in air / ms^{-1}	Wavelength / m	Energy / J	Energy / eV	Part of em spectrum to which this quantum belongs

3. Sodium has a work function of 2.28 eV.
   (a) Explain what is meant by the term *work function* in the context of the photoelectric effect.
   (b) Calculate the minimum frequency of an incident photon which will just cause photoemission in sodium.
   (c) Find the maximum velocity of the photoelectrons emitted when freshly cut sodium metal is illuminated with monochromatic light of wavelength 500 nm.
   (d) Explain why many of the photoelectrons have a velocity less than this maximum.

4. A monochromatic beam of light of power 0.5 W and wavelength 400 nm illuminates a metal. The threshold wavelength for the metal is 5×10^{-7} m.
   (a) Calculate the number of photons which strike the metal every second.
   (b) Calculate the work function for the metal in electron volts.
   (c) Assuming that every incident photon liberates an electron, calculate the size of the photoelectric current which could be taken from the metal with this arrangement.

5. When a metal of work function 3 eV is illuminated with light of wavelength 400 nm a photoelectric current of 1 µA can be detected. What current would be detected if the incident beam was of twice the intensity and of wavelength 600 nm?

6. Cesium has a work function of 2.1 eV. Find the maximum kinetic energy of the photoelectrons emitted when cesium is illuminated with light of wavelength 400 nm.

7. (a) What do the letters in the word "LASER" stand for?
   (b) In the context of laser action explain what is meant by:
       (i)   the ground state of an atom;
       (ii) an excited state;
       (iii) a population inversion;
       (iv) optical pumping;
       (v)   a metastable state.
   (c) A helium-neon gas laser of the type used in schools has a power of 1 mW. At a distance of 2 m from the laser, the diameter of the beam is about 2 mm. Calculate the power density of the beam (power per unit area) at this distance and comment on the result. For the purposes of comparison, the light intensity on the surface of a desk from a normal lamp is about 0.2 Wm^{-2}.

8. The diagram shows some of the energy levels in the hydrogen atom.

   (a) Why are all the energy levels negative?

   (b) Which of the energy levels above is known as the "ground state"?

   (c) An electron in an excited state relaxes to the –3.4 eV state in a single transition. Using the figures shown in the diagram, show that regardless of the level from which the electron relaxes, the radiation emitted is in the visible part of the electromagnetic spectrum.

   (d) How many different spectral lines are possible when transitions occur between the energy levels in the diagram?

   ```
   ------------------------------------------
   –0.54 eV ————————————————————————
   –0.85 eV ————————————————————————

   –1.5 eV  ————————————————————————

   –3.4 eV  ————————————————————————




   –13.6 eV ————————————————————————
   ```

9. In an X-ray tube electrons are accelerated to very high speeds and then made to fall incident on a metal target.

   (a) Why is it important that the target material is a good conductor of heat and has a high melting point?

   (b) Both copper and aluminium are good conductors of heat and have high melting points. Why then is copper sometimes used in X-ray tubes, but aluminium is never used?

   (c) The continuous X-ray spectrum is produced by a process called braking radiation (or Bremsstrahlung). Describe what is meant by *braking radiation*.

   (d) Describe the process of X-ray production in terms of electron movement between energy levels.

10. (a) State a typical wavelength for X-rays.

    (b) An electron in an X-ray tube has a kinetic energy of 10 keV. Assume that all of this energy is converted into the energy of a single X-ray photon. Calculate the wavelength of this X-ray photon.

11. (a) What is meant by the letters CT in "CT scanning" in the context of medical diagnostics?

    (b) State one similarity in the radiation used to diagnose broken bones and that used in a CT scan.

    (c) State one difference in the radiation used in a conventional X-ray photograph and that used in a CT scan.

    (d) When taking an X-ray of the chest of a female, radiographers sometimes place a heavy lead-lined sheet over the patient's pelvis. Why do they do this?

    (e) Why is a computer essential in CT scanning, but not when taking a conventional X-ray photograph?

12. A physicist illuminates a metal surface of work function, W, with light of a particular frequency, f. She then measures the maximum kinetic energy, E_k, of the emitted photoelectrons. The results are shown in the table below.

Frequency, f / Hz	6.0×10^{14}	6.2×10^{14}	6.4×10^{14}	6.6×10^{14}	6.8×10^{14}	7.0×10^{14}
E_k / J	2.6×10^{-20}	3.9×10^{-20}	5.2×10^{-20}	6.6×10^{-20}	7.9×10^{-20}	9.2×10^{-20}

   (a) Write down the equation for E_k in terms of f, W and the Planck constant, h.

   (b) Plot the graph of E_k (vertical axis) against f (horizontal axis).

   (c) Determine the gradient of your graph and state its unit.

   (d) What value do these data give for the Planck constant, h?

   (e) State or calculate the value of E_k when f = 0 and comment on its significance.

Unit 2.6 (AS 2)
Wave-particle duality

1. Explain what physicists mean when they talk about "particle-wave duality".

2. Some experimental observations can only be explained satisfactorily using a wave model, others require a particle model and a few can be explained using either model. Identify the model which is best used to explain the following phenomena, by copying the table and ticking the appropriate boxes:

Observation:	Refraction	Polarisation	Diffraction of light	Photoelectric effect	Young's fringes
Wave Model					
Particle Model					

3. The wave nature of moving electrons was first demonstrated experimentally by Davisson & Germer when they made fast electrons fall incident on a crystal of nickel and obtained a diffraction pattern on a photographic film.
    (a) Describe the diffraction pattern obtained in this way.
    (b) What was causing the electrons to diffract?
    (c) Why was it necessary to use *fast* electrons?
    (d) What part of the electromagnetic spectrum had a wavelength similar to these fast electrons?

4. The dual nature of fast electrons is shown in the de Broglie equation.
    (a) State the de Broglie equation and show how it links the particle and wave nature of fast electrons.
    (b) The wavelength of moving electrons depends on their speed. Copy the graph axes shown and sketch the graph which shows the nature of this relationship.

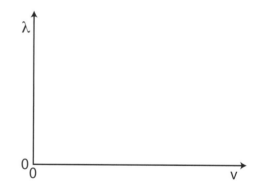

5. A beam of protons and a beam of electrons are both accelerated to a speed of 2 Mms^{-1}.
    (a) Which particles have the longer de Broglie wavelength?
    (b) Calculate the ratio of the wavelength of the electrons to that of the protons.

6. A physicist requires a beam of electrons to have a de Broglie wavelength of 0.122 nm. Calculate:
    (a) the speed of these electrons;
    (b) the energy of one of the electrons in joules;
    (c) the potential difference through which the electrons were accelerated.

7. Calculate the linear momentum of a photon of frequency 5×10^{14} Hz.

8. Explain why the wave nature of a car of mass 800 kg moving at 15 ms^{-1} is never observed.

9. Calculate the wavelength of an electron with an energy of 100 eV.

10. A subatomic particle moving with a speed of 300 ms^{-1} has a de Broglie wavelength of 2.42×10^{-6} m. What is the particle most likely to be? Justify your answer.

11. Find an expression for the de Broglie wavelength of an electron in terms of its mass, m, its kinetic energy, E and the Planck constant, h.

12. A physicist tabulates the de Broglie wavelength, λ, of a moving particle for different values of its speed. Her results are shown below. The last row is left blank for your use.

Wavelength, λ /nm	400	350	300	250	200	150
Speed/ ms^{-1}	1820	2080	2430	2910	3640	4850

(a) Use the data to plot a suitable straight line graph from which the mass of the particle can be obtained.
(b) From your graph determine the particle's mass.
(c) Identify the particle.

Unit 2.7 (AS 2)
Astronomy

1. An express train's hooter emits a constant note of frequency 600 Hz as it approaches a station. A stationary observer on the station platform detects a sound of frequency 660 Hz. If the speed of sound is 330 ms^{-1}, calculate:
   (a) the speed of the train;
   (b) the frequency of the sound detected by the observer when the train passes the station and continues on its journey.

2. A loudspeaker, which emits a note of frequency 250 Hz, is whirled in a vertical circle of radius 1.00 m at a constant speed of 2.00 ms^{-1}. Calculate the maximum and minimum frequencies detected by a stationary observer if the speed of sound is 330 ms^{-1}. Give your answers to 3 significant figures.

3. An astronomer is trying to confirm that the Andromeda Galaxy is approaching our galaxy (The Milky Way) at a speed of 110 km s^{-1}. The H-alpha line in the visible spectrum of hydrogen is observed in the laboratory to have a wavelength of 656.0 nm. What wavelength would the astronomer expect to see for the H-alpha line from Andromeda? Give your answer in nm to 1 decimal place.

4. Around the middle of the 20th century the American cosmologist Allan Sandage suggested that the age of the universe was 20 billion years (1 year $\approx 3.16\times10^7$ s). What value would this give for the value of the Hubble parameter, assuming that it is constant? Take a billion to be 1×10^9.

5. Our Sun is rotating. Light waves received on Earth from opposite ends of a diameter across the Sun show equal but opposite Doppler shifts. In the laboratory the F-line of hydrogen has a wavelength of 486.1 nm. The difference in the wavelengths of the F-line from one extreme end of the Sun's diameter and the corresponding wavelength in the laboratory is 3.2 pm. Calculate the relative speed of the Sun at one end of the diameter with respect to a fixed observer on Earth.

6. A star is moving away from the Earth with a speed of 3.6×10^5 ms^{-1}.
   (a) Use Hubble's Law to find its distance from the Earth in km.
   (b) Calculate the z-parameter for the star.
   Take H_o as 2.4×10^{-18} s^{-1} and assume that it has remained constant.

7. A *quasar* is a quasi-stellar radio source. They are found very far from Earth and have enormous speed. One such quasar, which emits visible light, has a z-parameter of 6.3. Explain briefly why it is inappropriate to use the equation:
$$z = \frac{\Delta\lambda}{\lambda} = \frac{\Delta f}{f} = \frac{v}{c}$$
   to calculate its speed.

8. A distant galaxy has a z-parameter (redshift) of 0.40.
    (a) Estimate the galaxy's speed of recession.
    (b) Use Hubble's Law to estimate the distance between the Earth and that galaxy. Give your answer in light years, given that 1 light year is 9.5×10^{15} m
    (c) Suggest why your answers to (a) and (b) can only be estimates.
    Take H_o as 2.4×10^{-18} s^{-1} and assume that it has remained constant.

9. Cosmologists believe that the rate at which the Universe expanded in the period shortly after the Big Bang was much greater than the rate at which it is expanding today. Our present value of the Hubble parameter is based on observations made on galaxies today. What implications do these observations have on our value of H_o and our estimate of the actual age of the Universe?

10 Binary stars are two stars which rotate around a common centre of mass. Suggest why astronomers looking at the light from a binary star over time are likely to see both red-shift and blue-shift.

11. An aeroplane flies at a constant speed and at a constant altitude. Its engine has a characteristic frequency, f_s. As it approaches a stationary observer in a hot-air balloon, the sound of its engine appears to be 220 Hz. After it passes the balloon, the sound from the engine of the aeroplane appears to be 110 Hz.
    (a) Taking the speed of sound as 330 ms^{-1} and using classical Doppler equations, calculate:
        (i)   the speed of the aeroplane, v.
        (ii) the frequency of the sound emitted by the aeroplane.
    (b) What assumption have you made in these calculations?

12. A motorist accelerates away from traffic lights at a steady rate. A sounder on the top of the car emits sound continually at a frequency, f_o, of 680 Hz. A scientist, standing at the traffic lights, records both the speed of the motorist and the frequency of the sound received. Some of her results are shown below.

Speed v / ms^{-1}	0	5	10	15	20	25
Frequency, f / Hz	680	670	661	651	642	633
f^{-1} / s $\times 10^{-3}$	1.47	1.49	1.51	1.54	1.56	1.58

(a) Plot the graph of speed, v / ms^{-1} (y-axis) against f^{-1} / s^{-1} (x-axis) and draw the line of best fit.
(b) Find the gradient of the graph and state its unit.
(c) Starting with the classical Doppler equation for the frequency received by a stationary observer from a receding source, show that:

$$v = v_w \cdot \frac{f_o}{f} - v_w$$

where v_w is the speed of sound in air and the other symbols are as defined above.
(d) By comparing your graph with the equation for a straight line, calculate the speed of sound in air.

AS 3
Practical Techniques and Data Analysis

1. When a car moves it experiences a frictional force due to air resistance. This is commonly known as drag. The magnitude of the drag force F_d / N is given by:

    $$F_d = \frac{1}{2} \rho v^2 C_d A$$

    where:
    ρ = density of the air / kg m^{-3}
    v = velocity of the car / ms^{-1}
    C_d = drag coefficient – a constant with no units
    A = drag area / m^2 – the area the car presents to the air
    (a) Show that this equation has the same base units on both sides.
    (b) For a particular car, what graph would you plot to show a linear relationship between the drag force and the velocity of the car? Assume that the density of the air is constant.
    (c) The product $C_d A$ is known as the drag area. The Toyota Prius has a drag area of 0.58 m^2 and the Land Rover Discovery has a drag area of 1.62 m^2. Sketch the shape of the graph you would obtain for each car, labelling each graph. Label each axis with the quantity and the appropriate unit.

2. A uniform beam of weight W is pivoted as shown in the diagram. A force meter attached at one end allows the upward tension force T to be measured. A force F is moved along the beam. When the beam is balanced the distance D and the tension force T are noted. This is repeated for a range of values of D.

    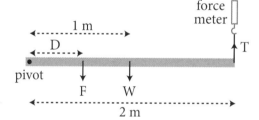

    (a) When the beam is in equilibrium write down an equation showing the clockwise and anticlockwise moments.
    (b) Identify the independent and dependent variables in this investigation.
    (c) What graph would you plot to obtain a linear graph for the variables you have listed in part (b)?
    (d) Sketch the sketch you have stated in part (c).
    (e) Explain how the values of F and W could be obtained from the graph.

3. A trolley is allowed to run down a slope onto a horizontal surface. The trolley is released from different heights H. The distance it travels along the horizontal until it stops, s, is measured. The initial potential energy of the trolley is mgH which is converted into kinetic energy as it moves down the slope. The subsequent loss of potential energy equals the work done by the friction force F:

    $$mgH = Fs$$

    The results of the investigation are shown below.

H / m	0.2	0.4	0.6	0.8	1.0
s / m	0.45	0.92	1.31	1.95	2.05

    (a) Plot a suitable linear graph to show the relationship between H and s.
    (b) The friction force slowing the trolley has an average value of 0.8 N. Use the graph to find the mass of the trolley.

4. The diagram show two spheres which are about to have an elastic collision. The velocity of A before collision is u, and B is stationary. The masses of A and B are m and M respectively. The velocity of A after collision is v, and that of B is V. The velocity of A after collision is given by:

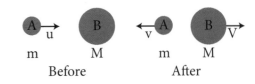

$$v = \frac{u(m - M)}{(m + M)}$$

The velocity of B after collision is given by:

$$V = \frac{2mu}{(m + M)}$$

(a) Using a spreadsheet calculate the velocity of A and B after collision. Give A a constant mass of 1 kg and a constant initial velocity of 1 ms⁻¹. Vary the mass of B starting with 1 kg, then 50 kg and then in steps of 50 kg up to to 300 kg.

(b) Comment on the value of v when the spheres both have a mass of 1 kg.

(c) Comment on what would be observed as the mass of sphere B is increased.

(d) What is observed when the mass of B is 1000 kg?

5. A trolley is allowed to move from rest down a runway. The time to travel a measured distance, S, is measured three times and an average time, T, taken. The results are shown in the table below.

S / cm	20	40	60	80	100
T / s	3.7	5.2	6.3	7.3	8.2

(a) Explain why the time is taken three times and an average found.

(b) Plot a suitable **linear** graph using results of this experiment. You may wish to copy the table and use the blank spaces in the table for any additional calculations you need.

(c) Use the graph to find the acceleration of the trolley down the runway. Give your answer in cms⁻².

6. A trolley is allowed to move from rest down a runway. A motion sensor is placed at various distances, S, along the runway and measures the velocity, V, of the trolley as it passes. The results are shown in the table below.

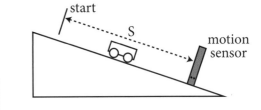

S / m	0.15	0.30	0.45	0.60	0.75
V / ms⁻¹	1.20	1.65	2.00	2.35	2.60

(a) Plot a suitable **linear** graph using results of this experiment. You may wish to use the blank spaces in the table for any additional calculations you need.

(b) Use the graph to find the acceleration of the trolley down the runway.

7. A trolley is allowed to move from rest down a runway. A motion sensor placed 2.0 m from the start and measures the velocity, V, of the trolley as it passes. The tilt of the runway is changed and the angle it makes with the horizontal measured. The experiment is repeated for angles from 5° to 25°. The results are shown in the table below. Ignore friction in your analysis.

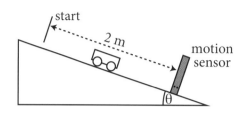

θ / °	5	10	15	20	25
V / ms⁻¹	1.8	2.5	3.1	3.5	3.9

Opposite is a simplified diagram of the apparatus. The trolley is represented by a dot.

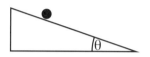

(a) Copy the diagram and mark on it the force that causes the trolley to accelerate down the runway.

(b) Apply Newton's second law of motion to this situation and derive an equation linking the final velocity of the trolley and the angle of the runway θ.

(c) Plot a suitable **linear** graph using results of this experiment. You may wish to use the blank spaces in the table for any additional calculations you need.

(d) Use the graph to find the acceleration of free fall.

8. A battery and a number of identical resistors are connected as shown opposite. The current, I, flowing in the circuit is measured as the number of identical resistors connected in parallel is increased. The potential difference, V, is constant.

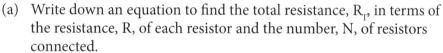

(a) Write down an equation to find the total resistance, R_T, in terms of the resistance, R, of each resistor and the number, N, of resistors connected.

(b) Write down an equation to find the current I in terms of the potential difference V, the resistance of each resistor, R, and the number of resistors connected in parallel.

(c) Identify the dependent and independent variables in this investigation.

(d) What linear graph would you plot to show the relationship between the variables stated above.

(e) Explain how you use the graph and any other measurement to find the value of R.

9. A battery and a number of identical resistors are connected as shown opposite. The current, I, flowing in the circuit is measured as the number of identical resistors connected in parallel is increased. The potential difference, V, is constant.

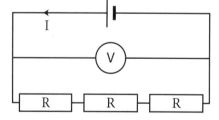

(a) Write down an equation to find the total resistance, R_T, in terms of the resistance R of each resistor and the number, N, of resistors connected.

(b) Write down an equation to find the current, I, in terms of the potential difference, V, the resistance of each resistor, R, and the number of resistors connected in series.

(c) Identify the dependent and independent variables in this investigation.

(d) What linear graph would you plot to show the relationship between the variables stated above.

(e) Explain how you use the graph and any other measurement to find the value of R.

10. A cell has an e.m.f., E, of 1.5 V and an internal resistance r of 0.5 Ω. It is connected to the circuit shown. The power P / W dissipated by the load resistor is given by the equation:

    $$P = \frac{E^2R}{(R + r)^2}$$

    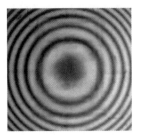

    (a) Using a spreadsheet calculate the power dissipated as the load resistance R / Ω is varied from 0.1 Ω to 1.5 Ω in steps of 0.1 Ω.
    (b) Using your results plot a graph of power dissipated P / W against the load resistance R / Ω.
    (c) Comment on your findings.

11. *Newton's Rings* is an example of interference of light reflected from the inner curved surface of a convex lens and the flat surface of a glass block on which the lens is placed. This arrangement is shown below.

    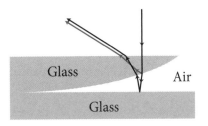

    The interference pattern consists of a series of bright and dark rings as shown above. The relationship between the radius of the mth bright fringe, r_m, and the number of the ring, m, is given by:

    $$r_m = \sqrt{(2m + 1)K}$$

    (a) Re-arrange the above equation so that a linear graph can be plotted to show the relationship between r_m and m. K is a constant in the above relationship.
    (b) Sketch the graph that would be obtained and explain how the value of the constant K can be obtained from the graph.

12. During an experimental measurement of the resistance of a thermistor the results below were recorded.

Temperature / °C	0	10	20	30	40	50
Resistance / kΩ	34	20	12.5	8.0	5.2	3.5

    The relationship between the resistance, R, in kΩ, of the thermistor and the temperature, θ, is approximately given by equation:

    $$R = 33.1 - 1.1\theta + 0.014\theta^2$$

    (a) Using the data in the table compare the value of R measured at 20°C with the value calculated using the equation above.
    (b) Calculate the percentage difference between these two values.

Answers

1.1 Physical Quantities

1. (a) $GPE = mgh = kg\ m^2 s^{-2}$
   (b) $D = M \div V = kg\ m^{-3}$
   (c) $P = F \div A = Nm^{-2} = kg\ m^{-1}s^{-2}$
   (d) $w = mg = kg\ ms^{-2}$
   (e) impulse = force $\times$ time = $kg\ ms^{-1}$
2. (a) $R = V \div I = (JC^{-1}) \div A = Nm\ C^{-1}\ A^{-1} = kg\ ms^{-2} \times m \times A^{-1}\ s^{-1}\ A^{-1} = kg\ m^2 A^{-2}\ s^{-3}$
   (b) $c = Q \div m\Delta\theta = J \div kg\ K = kg\ m^2\ s^{-2}\ kg^{-1}\ K^{-1} = m^2\ s^{-2}\ K^{-1}$
3. $a = (2\pi f)^2 \times x = 4\pi^2\ f^2\ x$.
   $4\pi^2$ has no units. LHS = ms^{-2}. RHS = s^{-2} m or ms^{-2}.
4. Young's Modulus E = Stress $\div$ Strain
   Stress = $F \div A = Nm^{-2} = kg\ ms^{-2}$
   Strain = $e \div L$ and so has no units
   Therefore base units of E = $kg\ m^{-1}\ s^{-2}$
5. $0.9\ fm = 0.9 \times 10^{-15}$ m
   volume of proton = $\frac{4}{3}\pi r^3 = \frac{4}{3} \times \pi \times (0.9 \times 10^{-15})^3 = 3.05 \times 10^{-45}$ m^3
   density = mass $\div$ volume = $1.67 \times 10^{-27} \div 3.05 \times 10^{-45} = 5.48 \times 10^{17}$ kg m^{-3}.
6. $50\ MT = 5 \times 10^7$ T, energy release = $5 \times 10^7 \times 4.2 \times 10^{12} \div 1 \times 10^3 = 2.1 \times 10^{17}$ J
7. (a) 1 inch = 2.54 cm, 1 thou = $\frac{1}{1000}$ of an inch = $\frac{2.54}{1000}$ cm = 2.54×10^{-3} cm = 25.4 μm
   (b) $F = ma$; 1 kg = 2 lb 3.274 oz, so 0.454 kg = 1 lb; 1 ft = 12 inches = 12 $\times$ 2.54 cm = 30.5 cm = 0.305 m
      1 poundal = 1 lb $\times$ 1 ft s^{-2} = 0.454 kg $\times$ 0.305 ms^{-2} = 0.138 N
8. 1 second of arc = 4.85×10^{-6} radians. 1.496×10^8 km = 1.496×10^{11} m
   $S = r\theta$, $1.496 \times 10^{11} = r \times 4.85 \times 10^{-6}$, $r = 3.085 \times 10^{16}$ m
   1 ly = $3 \times 10^8 \times 86400 \times 365 = 9.46 \times 10^{15}$ m
   1 pc = $3.085 \times 10^{16} \div 9.46 \times 10^{15} = 3.26$ ly
9. (a) $100\ fm^2 = 10\ fm \times 10\ fm = 10 \times 10^{-15}$ m $\times$ 10×10^{-15} m = 100×10^{-30} m^2 = 1×10^{-28} m^2
   (b) 100 barns = $100 \times 1 \times 10^{-28}$ m^2 = 1×10^{-26} m^2
      area = πr^2, $1 \times 10^{-26} = \pi r^2$, $r = 5.6 \times 10^{-14}$ m.
10. Energy and work have the same base units. Work = force $\times$ distance
    Acceleration is measured in ms^{-2}, acceleration = distance $\div$ time^2, so distance = acceleration $\times$ time^2
    Therefore work or energy = force $\times$ distance = $F \times A \times T^2$.
11. (a) Equatorial circumference = $2\pi \times 6378$ km = 4.008×10^4 km; $360° = 360 \times 60' = 2.16 \times 10^{4'}$
       1 nautical mile = circumference in km $\div$ length of 1 minute of arc = $4.008 \times 10^4 \div 2.16 \times 10^4 = 1.85$ km
    (b) 1.85 km = 1850 m; 1 hour = 3600 s; 1 nautical mile per hour = 1850 m $\div$ 3600 s
       15 knots = $15 \times 1850 \div 3600 = 7.7$ ms^{-1}.
12. (a) 5460.47 Å = 546.047×10^{-9} m, 1 Å = 1×10^{-10} m.
    (b) 630×10^{-9} m $\div 1 \times 10^{-10}$ m = 6300 Å

1.2 Vectors and Scalars

1. (a) A scalar has magnitude and a unit, a vector has magnitude, a unit and a direction.
   (b) Vectors: velocity ms^{-1}, acceleration ms^{-2}, force N, momentum kg ms^{-1}, impulse Ns.
      Scalars: mass kg, distance m, temperature K, density kg m^{-3}.
   (c) x-component = 25 cos 42° = 18.6 N; y-component = 25 sin 42° = 16.7 N

2. Resultant $= \sqrt{16^2 + 12^2} = 20$ N
    Tan of angle $= 12 \div 16$, angle $= 36.9°$

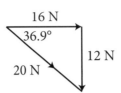

3. (a) Displacement $= \sqrt{300^2 + 400^2} = 500$ km
        Angle $= 36.9°$ east of north.

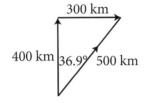

    (b) Resultant $= \sqrt{4^2 + 6^2} = 7.2$ ms^{-1}
        Angle $= 56.3°$ to vertical.

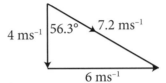

4. Vertical component of 8 N $= 8 \cos 60 = 4$ N (downward)
    Horizontal component of 8 N $= 8 \sin 60 = 6.9$ N
    The vertical resultant $= 1$ N (see diagram)
    The resultant force $= \sqrt{1^2 + 6.9^2} = 6.97$ N
    To find angle θ: $\tan \theta = 6.9 \div 1$, $\theta = 81.8°$

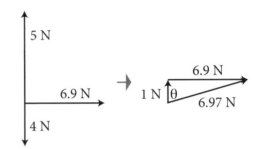

5.

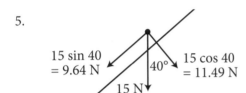

6. The system is in equilibrium so the horizontal components are equal:

    $T_1 \cos 60 = T_2 \cos 30$, so $\dfrac{T_1}{T_2} = \dfrac{0.866}{0.5} = 1.73$

7.

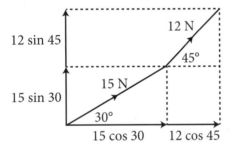

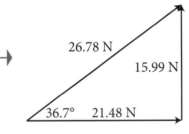

8. The system is in equilibrium so the vertical component of T $= 500$ N
    The horizontal component $= 1000$ N
    Hence tension $= \sqrt{500^2 + 1000^2} = 1118$ N
    Angle to the horizontal $= 63.4°$ by trigonometry

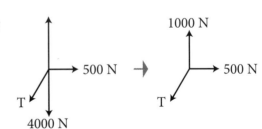

9. Final displacement $= 83.8$ km at an angle of $74.5°$
    See diagram for method.

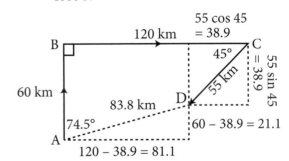

10. (a)

    (b)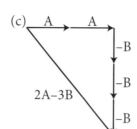

    (c)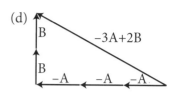

    (d)

11. Using the cosine rule: $a^2 = b^2 + c^2 - 2bc \cos A$
    $XY^2 = 1200^2 + 2000^2 - (2 \times 1200 \times 2000 \times \cos(110°))$
    $XY = 2.65 \times 10^3$ m
    Or by adding horizontal components:
    $XY = 1200 \cos 40° + 2000 \cos 30° = 919 + 1732 = 2651$ m

12. 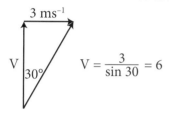 $V = \dfrac{3}{\sin 30} = 6$

1.3 Moments

1. Let D be the distance of the centre of gravity from P. Anticlockwise Moments about P = Clockwise Moments:
   $50 \times 2 = 12.0 \times 9.81 \times D$, so D = 0.85 m
2. Let the suspended weight be W. Take moments about P: $14 \times 9.81 \times 0.32 = W \times 0.85$, giving W = 51.7 N
3. (a) Product of the force and the perpendicular distance from the point.
   (b) (i) tan 30 = AC ÷ AD, so AC = AD tan 30 = 40 tan 30 = 2.31 m
       (ii) Take moments at B: the reaction forces at A and B have zero moment.
            The perpendicular distance from B to the wire = 3.73 m
            $500 \times 2 = \text{Tension} \times 3.73$, so Tension = 268.1 N
       (iii) Horizontal reaction at B = 268.1 × cos 30° = 232.1 N to the right.
       (iv) Vertical components of the reactions at A and B + Vertical component of tension = 500 N
            So vertical components of the reactions at A and B = 500 − 268.1 sin 30° = 366 N
4. Taking moments about the pivot: $22.4 = 64 \times d + 64 \times d$, so d = 17.5 cm.
   So distance between the two forces = 35.0 cm
5. (a) Take moments at the hinge: $500 \times 2 = T \times 4 \sin 40$, so T = 389 N
   (b) Tension has a vertical component T_y and a horizontal component T_x.
       Horizontal component of reaction force at hinge = R_x = 389 cos 40° = 298 N
       Vertical component of reaction force at hinge = R_y = 500 − 250 = 250 N (upwards)
       Reaction force at hinge = $\sqrt{250^2 + 298^2}$ = 389 N; angle = 40° to the right and above the horizontal.
6. (a) Take moments at B: $(2.0 \times R_A) = (0.5 \times 80 \times 9.81) + (0.5 \times 400)$, $R_A = 296$ N
       $R_A + R_B$ = downward force: 296 + R_B = 400 + (80 × 9.81), so R_B = 889 N
   (b) Let distance from Y be y. When it tilts $R_A = 0$, so by taking moments about B:
       $(1.5 − y) \times 80 \times 9.81 = 0.5 \times 400$, so (1.5 − y) = 0.25 and y = 1.25 m. So distance from Y = 1.25 m.
7. (a) Anticlockwise moments = (80 × 50) + (160 × 60) = 13 600 Nmm
       Clockwise moments = 200 × 120 sin 45° = 16971 Nmm
       Resultant moment = 16 971 − 13 600 = 3371 Nmm, clockwise.
   (b) Let the extra force be F. For equilibrium, anticlockwise moments = clockwise moments = 16 971 Nmm
       16 971 = (80 × (50+F)) + (160 × 60), F = 42.1 N
8. (a) Moment: F cos 40° × 0.25 = 50, so F = 261 N
   (b) Same moment for a smaller force. For example, 50 = F × 0.25, so F = 200 N
9. Anticlockwise Moments = Clockwise Moments: $4 \times 15 + 1 \times 65 = W \times 20 + 2 \times 35$, so W = 2.75 N
10. $M_2 \times 1 − M_1 \times 1 = 10 \times 2 = 20$ g
11. (a) $3 \times 12 = W \times 8 + 1 \times 28$, so W = 1 N
    (b) $(3 + 1 + 1) \times 15 = 1 \times 5 + 25 \times F$, so F = 70 ÷ 25 = 2.8 N
12. (a) $6 \times 25 = 3 \times 10 + W \times 30$, so W = 4 N
    (b) $6 \times 20 = 3 \times 10 + W \times 30$, so W = 3 N. Upthrust = 4 − 3 = 1 N

1.4 Linear motion

1. (a)   Distance = $2\pi r$ = 31.4 m. Displacement = 0.
    (b)   Speed = distance ÷ time = 31.4 ÷ 10 = 3.14 ms^{-1}
    (c)   0 ms^{-1} because average velocity = displacement ÷ time, and displacement = 0.
2. (a)   Using s = ut + ½at² gives: t = 3.19 s; Then using v = u + at gives: v = 31.3 ms^{-1}
    (b)   (i)   Using v² = u² – 2gs gives s = 1.27 m. Therefore max height = 200 + 1.27 = 201.27 m
          (ii)   Time to reach max height: v = u + at, 0 = 5 – 9.8t, t = 0.51 s
                 Time to reach ground from max height: s = ut + ½at², 201.27 = 0t + ½ × 9.81 × t², t = 6.41 s
                 Total time from leaving the helicopter = 0.51 + 6.41 = 6.92 s
          (iii) Using v² = u² – 2as: v² = 0² + 2 × 9.81 × (201.27 – 100), v = 44.6 ms^{-1}
3. (a)   Draw a graph of s against t² and measure its gradient s ÷ t². Gradient = ½a, so a = 1.96 ms^{-2}.
    (b)   Average velocity = 2.5 ÷ 1.6 = 1.56 ms^{-1}
          Final velocity = 2 × average velocity = 3.12 ms^{-1}
4.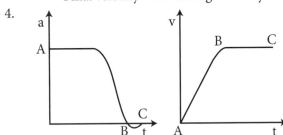
5. Count squares. Each complete square = 1 ms^{-1} × 1 s = 1 m. Answer approx 59 m.
6. Find the area of each section. Above the time axis is positive displacement, below is negative.
    Answer 9.5 m to the right of O.
7. (a)   Time for A: 1000 ÷ 20 = 50 s, Time for B using s = ut + ½at²: 1000 = 0 + ½ × 1 × t² giving t = 44.7 s
          Time for C: Using v² = u² + 2as gives v = 34.7ms^{-1};
          then using s = ut + ½at²: 1000 = ½ (2+ 34.7) × t, so t = 54.5 s. So B wins the race.
    (b)   Distance travelled by A = 20 × 44.7 = 894 m
          Distance travelled by C = 2 × 44.7 + ½ × 0.6 × 44.7² = 689 m
8.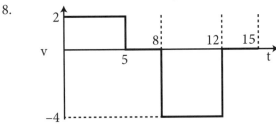
9. Velocity v = u – gt = 15 – 9.81 × 2.2 = –6.6 ms^{-1} (moving down)
    Either Height (displacement) s = ut – ½ gt² = 15 × 2.2 – ½ × 9.81 × 2.2² = 9.3 m
    or Time to reach max height: v = u + gt; 0 = 15 – 9.81t; t = 1.53 s.
    Max height using v² = u² + 2gs; 0² = 15² + 2 × –9.81 × s, s = 11.5 m
    Time from max height to 2.2 s = 2.2 – 1.53 = 0.67 s
    Distance fallen in 0.67 s using s = ut – ½ gt² gives s = 2.2 m
    Height above ground is 11.5 – 2.2 = 9.3 m
10. (a)   112 kmh^{-1} = 31.1 ms^{-1}· Reaction time = 21 ÷ 31.1 = 0.68 s
    (b)   Using v² = u² – 2as: 0 = 31.1² – 2 × a × 75, a = 6.4 ms^{-2}
11. (a)   Car A using s = ut + ½ at²: s = 0 + ½ × 1.5 × 10² = 75 m.
          Velocity after 10 s is 15 ms^{-1}. Distance travelled at constant velocity = 30 × 15 = 450 m
          Distance travelled after 40 s = 75 + 450 = 525m
          Car B using s = ut + ½ at²: s = 0 + ½ × 1 × 12² = 72 m.
          Velocity after 12 s is 12 ms^{-1}. Distance travelled at constant velocity = 28 × 12 = 336 m
          Distance travelled after 40 s = 72 + 336 = 408 m
    (b)   Separation = 525 – 408 = 117 m, so A travels further.

(c)

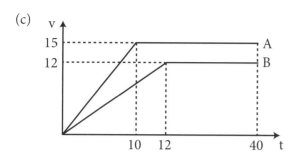

12. (a)   Using $v^2 = u^2 - 2as$: $40^2 = u^2 + 2 \times 9.81 \times 50$, giving $u = 24.9$ ms^{-1}
     (b)   Using $v = u + at$: $40 = 24.9 + 9.81 \times t$, giving $t = 1.54$ s

1.5 Dynamics

1.   Time to fall 2.0 m from rest = time to travel 4.0 m horizontally.
     $2 = \frac{1}{2} gt^2$, so $t = 0.64$ s. Horizontal velocity = $4.0 \div 0.64 = 6.25$ ms^{-1}.
2.   (a)   Initial vertical velocity = $u \sin\theta$, at maximum height vertical velocity = 0
           using $v = u - gT$: $0 = u \sin\theta$ giving $T = u \sin\theta \div g$
     (b)   Time to reach ship is equal to time to reach the maximum height + time to fall from the maximum height
           $T_{of} = 2u \sin\theta \div g$
     (c)   Horizontal distance $R = T_{of} \times$ horizontal velocity = $2u \sin\theta \div g \times u \cos\theta = 2u^2 \sin\theta\cos\theta \div g$
           $R = u^2 \sin2\theta \div g$
     (d) $600 = 90^2 \sin2\theta \div 9.81$, $\sin2\theta = 0.7267$, $2\theta = 46.6°$ and $133.4°$, $\theta = 23.3°$ and $66.7°$.
3.   (a)   Initial vertical velocity = $30 \sin 40° = 19.3$ ms^{-1}
           Initial horizontal velocity = $30 \cos 40° = 23.0$ ms^{-1}
     (b)   Time spent in the air = $2 \times$ initial vertical velocity $\div$ g, so $2 \times 19.3 \div 9.81 = 3.9$ s
     (c)   Vertical height = $\frac{1}{2}(u + v) \div 1.95 = 18.8$ m
           $v^2 - u^2 = 2gs$, so vertical height $s = (v^2 - u^2) \div 2g = (0^2 - 19.3^2) \div 2 \times -9.81 = 19.0$ m
     (d)   Range = horizontal velocity $\times$ time = $23.0 \times 3.9 = 89.7$ m
     (e)   Vertical velocity at time $t = 3$: $v = u + at = 19.3 + (-9.81 \times 3) = -10.4$ ms^{-1}
           $\sin\theta$ = vertical velocity $\div$ horizontal velocity = $-3.2 \div 23.0$, so $\theta = 8.0°$
           The minus indicates a downward velocity. $\tan\theta = 10.4 \div 23.0$ giving $\theta = 24.3°$
4.   Vertical component of initital velocity = $8 \sin\theta$ ms^{-1}.
     $v^2 = u^2 + 2gs$, so $0 = (8 \sin\theta)^2 + (2 \times -9.81 \times 2.2)$. $\theta = 55°$
5.   (a)   Vertical component of initial velocity = $40 \sin 60°$
           $v^2 = u^2 + 2gs$, so $0 = 34.6^2 + (2 \times -9.81 \times s)$. $s = 61$ m
           Maximum height above the sea = $50 + 61 = 111$ m
     (b)   Vertical component of velocity when it strikes the sea = v
           $v^2 = u^2 + 2gs = 0 + (2 \times 9.81 \times 111)$. $v = 46.7$ ms^{-1}
           Horizontal component of velocity when it strikes the sea = $40 \cos 60° = 20$ ms^{-1}
           Using Pythagoras' theorem, velocity as it reaches the sea = 50.8 ms^{-1}
           (Angle $\tan\theta = 46.7 \div 20$, $\theta = 66.8°$ below the horizontal)
6.   (a) $s = u^2 + \frac{1}{2}at^2$, so $25.0 = 0 + (\frac{1}{2} \times 9.81 \times t^2)$. $t = 2.26$ s
     (b) s = velocity $\times$ time = $12.0 \times 2.26 = 27.12$ m
     (c)   Horizontal velocity = constant 12.0 ms^{-1}. Vertical component of velocity when it strikes the sea = v
           $v = u + at = 0 + (9.81 \times 2.26) = 22.2$ ms^{-1}
           Using Pythagoras' theorem, velocity as it reaches the sea = 25.2 ms^{-1}
           (Angle $\tan\theta = 22.2 \div 12$, $\theta = 61.6°$ below the horizontal)
7.   50 m = horizontal velocity $\times$ time of flight
     $50 = (30 \cos\theta) \times (2 \times \dfrac{30 \sin\theta}{g}) = 30^2 \sin 2\theta \div g$ (using the rule: $\sin 2x = 2 \sin x \cos x$)

     $\sin 2\theta = 0.545$, so $2\theta = 33.0°$ and $147.0°$. Therefore $\theta = 16.5°$ and $73.5°$.
8.   (a)   Using $s = ut + \frac{1}{2} gt^2$: $200 = 20t + (\frac{1}{2} \times 9.81 \times t^2)$. Solving this quadratic equation gives $t = 4.67$ s
     (b)   Range = horizontal velocity $\times$ time = $40 \cos 30° \times 4.67 = 161.8$ m
     (c)   Horizontal velocity = $40 \cos 30° = 34.6$ ms^{-1}
           Initial vertical velocity = $40 \sin 30° = 20$ ms^{-1}

Vertical velocity at time t = 2: v = u + at = 20 + (9.81 × 2) = 39.6 ms^{-1}
Using Pythagoras' theorem, velocity at time t = 2 is $\sqrt{39.6^2 + 34.6^2}$ = 52.6 ms^{-1}
Angle tan θ = 39.6 ÷ 34.6, θ = 48.9° below the horizontal.

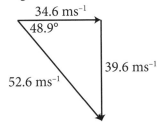

9. (a) Horizontal component = 40 cos 50° = 25.7 ms^{-1}
        Initial vertical component = 40 sin 50° = 30.6 ms^{-1}
        Vertical component at time t = 2.5: v = u + gt = 30.6 + (−9.81 × 2.5) = 6.1 ms^{-1}
    (b) Using Pythagoras' theorem, velocity at time t = 2.5 is $\sqrt{25.7^2 + 6.1^2}$ = 26.4 ms^{-1}
        Angle tan θ = 6.1 ÷ 25.7, θ = 13.4° above the horizontal.
    (c) Height at time t = 2.5: s = ut + ½gt^2 = (30.6 × 2.5) + (½ × −9.81 × 2.5^2) = 45.8 m
10. (a) H = ut + ½gt^2 = 0 + (½ × 9.81 × 8^2) = 314 m
    (b) Vertical component at time t = 8: v = u + gt = 0 + (9.81 × 8) = 78.5 ms^{-1}
        Using Pythagoras' theorem, velocity at time t = 8 is $\sqrt{78.5^2 + 100^2}$ = 127.1 ms^{-1}
        Angle tan θ = 78.5 ÷ 100, θ = 38.1° below the horizontal.
    (c) Distance = D = velocity × time = 100 × 8 = 800 m
11. (a) Ascending, using v = u + gt: 18 = 35 sin 50 + (−9.81 × t) giving t = 0.9 s
        Descending: 18 = 35 sin 50 + (−9.81 × t) giving t = 4.6 s
    (b) Ascending displacement = velocity × time = 35 cos 50 × 0.9 = 20.25 m
        Descending displacement = 35 cos 50 × 4.6 = 103.5 m
12. (a) Time to reach max height t = $\dfrac{u \sin θ}{g}$. If both reach max height at the same time then:
        $\dfrac{20 \sin 60}{9.81} = \dfrac{u_A \sin 45}{9.81}$ giving u_A = 24.49 ms^{-1}
    (b) Range$_A$ = horizontal velocity × time of flight = (20 cos 60) × (2 × $\dfrac{20 \sin 60}{9.81}$) = 35.31 m
        Range$_B$ = horizontal velocity × time of flight, so:
        35.31 = (u$_B$ cos 45) × (2 × $\dfrac{u_B \sin 45}{9.81}$) giving u$_B$= 18.61 ms^{-1}.

1.6 Newton's laws

1. (a) Component of weight acting down the slope = mg sin 25 = 0.4 × 9.81 × sin 25 = 1.66 N
        Resultant force = 1.66 − friction = 1.66 − 1.20 = 0.46 N
        F = ma, so acceleration = F ÷ m = 0.46 ÷ 0.4 = 1.15 ms^{-2}
    (b) Resultant force = 0 so acceleration = 0.
2. (a) (i) The action force is the pulling force that the tractor exerts on the trailer and the reaction
                force is the pulling force that the trailer exerts on the tractor. These two forces are equal, act in
                opposite directions and act on different objects.
        (ii) The action force is the gravitational force that the Sun exerts on the Earth, the reaction force is the
                gravitational force that the Earth exerts on the Sun. The two force are equal, act in opposite directions
                and act on different objects. Although the Sun has a mass approximately one million times that of the
                Earth the gravitational force is proportional to the product of the two masses.
    (b) When one object exerts a force on a second object, the second object simultaneously exerts a force equal in
        magnitude and opposite in direction on the first object.
3. Resultant resistive force = 250 + 75 = 325 N. Total mass = 850 + 70 = 920 kg
    Resultant forward force = ma = 920 × 3.4 = 3128 N
    Force of engine = resultant forward force + resultant resistive force = 3128 + 325 = 3453 N
4. (a) F = ma, so a = F ÷ m = 20 ÷ (2 + 4) = 3.33 ms^{-2}
    (b) The only force on the 2 kg mass is the tension T = ma = 2 × 3.33 = 6.66 N

5. F_{AB} is the force that A exerts on B, and F_{BA} is the force that B exerts on A.
    $F_{AB} = -F_{BA}$. Action and reaction are equal and opposite. Duration of collision = Δt.
    Impulse of A on B = $I_{AB} = F_{AB}\Delta t$
    Impulse of B on A = $I_{BA} = -F_{BA}\Delta t$
    Total impulse = 0 therefore momentum change = 0

6. Additional force = momentum change of the sand per second = $10 \times 8 = 80$ N

7. (a) Total resistive force at 10 ms^{-1} = $10 + 0.15v^2 = 10 + 15 = 25$ N
        F = ma, so a = F ÷ m = $(50 - 25) \div 80 = 0.31$ ms^{-2}
    (b) Maximum speed is when total resitive force = maximum forward force
        $10 + 0.15v^2 = 100$, giving v = 24.5 ms^{-1}

8. (a) Newton's First Law: a body moving with constant velocity will continue to do so unless a resultant
        force acts on it.
    (b) Newton's Second Law : the acceleration of a body is inversely proportional to its mass, directly
        proportional to the resultant force acting on it and takes place in the same direction as the
        resultant force.
    (c) Mass of man = $750 \div 9.81 = 76.45$ kg. Let upward force = R.
        R – downard force of gravity = ma
        R – $76.45 \times 1.62 = 76.45 \times 0.5$
        R = 162.08 N

9. (a) Tension in cables = Weight of lift + force due to acceleration
        = mg + ma = $(300 + 65) \times 9.81 + (300 + 65) \times 0.3 = 3690$ N
        Tension in each cable = $3690 \div 4 = 9.23 \times 10^2$ N
    (b) Upward force = Weight of person + force due to acceleration
        F = mg + ma = $65 \times 9.81 + 65 \times 0.3 = 6.57 \times 10^2$ N

10. Resultant horizontal force = $4 \cos 45° + 8 - 10 \cos 30 = 2.17$ N
    Resultant vertical force = $6 + 4 \sin 45° - 10 \sin 30 - 12 = -8.17$ N
    Total resultant force (by Pythagoras' theorem) = 8.45 N
    Acceleration = F ÷ m = $8.45 \div 4.0 = 2.11$ ms^{-2}
    Angle = $\tan^{-1}(-8.17 \div 2.17) = 75.1°$ below the horizontal

11. (a) Let T be the tension in the string. Calculating F = ma for each object gives two equations:
        $T - (8 \times 9.81) = -8a$ (1)
        $T - (5 \times 9.81) = 5a$ (2)
        Subtracting (1) from (2) gives a = 2.26 ms^{-2}
    (b) Substituting the value for a into (1) gives $T - (8 \times 9.81) = -8 \times 2.26$, giving T = 60.4 N

12. Constant speed means friction = driving force = 2000 N
    Acceleration force when climbing hill = F_{res} = ma = $1500 \times 0.5 = 750$ N
    Additional force opposing the motion is the component of the weight down the slope
    = $mg \sin \theta = 1500 \times 9.81 \times (1 \div 10) = 1472$ N
    Total driving force = force of friction + force of weight down the slope + acceleration force
    = $2000 + 1472 + 750 = 4222$ N

1.7 Linear momentum

1. (a) Momentum before collision = momentum after
        $0.005 \times 300 = 0.505 \times V_A$
        giving V_A = 2.97 ms^{-1}
    (b) Using the Principle of Conservation of Momentum
        $0.505 \times 2.97 = (0.5 + 0.505) \times V_B$
        giving V_B = 1.49 ms^{-1}
    (c) E_K of bullet = ½ mv^2 = ½ $(0.005) \times 300^2 = 225$ J
        E_K of bullet and block A = ½ $(0.505) \times 2.97^2 = 2.23$ J
        so kinetic energy is not conserved, therefore the collision is inelastic.
        After blocks A and B collide E_K = ½$(0.5+0.505) \times 1.49^2 = 1.12$ J
        E_K is not conserved so this second collision is also inelastic.

2. (a) Impulse = momentum change = $1200 \times 13.5 = 1.62 \times 10^4$ Ns
    (b) Driver decelerates from 13.5 ms^{-1} to zero in a distance of 0.1 m.
        Using $v^2 = u^2 - 2as$ gives a deceleration = 911 ms^{-2}. Then, F = ma = $60 \times 911 = 5.47 \times 10^4$ N.

      (c)   Using $v^2 = u^2 - 2as$ with $s = 0.02$ m we get $a = 4557$ ms^{-2} and $F = 2.73 \times 10^5$ N.

3.   First collision: $3000 \times 2 = 5500v$, giving $v = 1.09$ ms^{-1}

      Second collision: $5500 \times 1.09 - 5000 \times 5 = 10500v$, giving $v = -1.81$ ms^{-1}

      The minus indicates that the final velocity in the direction that the 5000 kg carriage was initially moving.

4.   (a)   The action of firing ions backwards produces a reaction force which propels the spacecraft forward.

      (b)   Thrust = momentum change per second, $0.5 = 2.2 \times 10^{-25} \times 3 \times 10^4 \times N$

            N is the number of ions ejected each second, $N = 7.58 \times 10^{19}$ s^{-1}.

      (c)   Hydrogen ions have a smaller mass so momentum change is smaller.

5.   (a)   Action and reaction: the momentum change per second of the water (action) produces a force in the opposite directon (reaction) on the firefighter.

      (b)   Force = momentum change per second = $50 \times 4 = 200$ N

6.   (a)   Total momentum is zero i.e. $3mu + mv_A = 0$, giving $v_A = 3u$ to the left

      (b) $m \times 3u + 3m \times u = 4mv_{common}$ giving $v_{common} = 1.5$ u

      (c)   The spring introduces an external force.

7.   Momentum change = force $\times$ time = $0.06 \times (25 - (-35)) = 250t$, giving $t = 1.44 \times 10^{-2}$ s

      The 35 ms^{-1} is negative since it is in the opposite direction.

8.   (a)   Principle of Conservation of momentum, $1200 \times 25 - 1800 \times 14 = 3000V_{combined}$

            $V_{combined} = 1.6$ ms^{-1}

      (b)   To the right i.e. the direction in which the 1200 kg car was initially moving.

      (c) E_K lost = E_K before the collision $-$ E_K after collision

            Remember kinetic energy is a scalar so direction is not important, the kinetic energies of the two cars must be added to find the kinetic before the collision.

            E_K lost = 5.47×10^5 J

9.   (a) $E_K = \frac{1}{2}mv^2$, $p = mv$

      (b) $E_K = \dfrac{p^2}{2m}$ or $E_K = \frac{1}{2}pv$

      (c) $\dfrac{p^2}{2m} = 20$, giving $m_{A+B} = 10$ kg, so $m_B = 5$ kg

            $m_{A+B} \times V = 20$, so $V = 2$ ms^{-1}, to the left.

10.   Velocity of recoil = $3 \times 10^{-2} \div 15 \times 10^{-3} = 2$ ms^{-1}

      Momentum of recoil = momentum of bullet: $2 \times 4.5 = 30 \times 10^{-3} \times V_{bullet}$ giving $V_{bullet} = 300$ ms^{-1}

11.   Impulse = Ft = area between graph and time axis = $\frac{1}{2} \times 6000 \times 1 \times 10^{-3} = 3$ Ns

      Impulse = momentum change: $3 = 44 \times 10^{-3} \times V$, giving $V = 68.2$ ms^{-1}

12.   (a)   Momentum before = $(1 \times 2) + (5 \times 1) = 7$ kg ms^{-1}

            Momentum after = $(1 \times V) + (5 \times 1.1) = 7$, giving $V = 1.5$ ms^{-1} to the right

      (b) E_K before = $\frac{1}{2}mv^2 + \frac{1}{2}mv^2 = (\frac{1}{2} \times 1 \times 2^2) + (\frac{1}{2} \times 5 \times 1^2) = 4.5$ J

            E_K after = $(\frac{1}{2} \times m \times 15^2) + (\frac{1}{2} \times 5 \times 1.1^2) = 4.15$ J

            The collision is inelastic since kinetic energy is not conserved.

1.8 Work done, potential and kinetic energy

1.   (a) E_K at P = 0.9 of E_p at O, so $\frac{1}{2}mv_p^2 = 0.9 \times m \times 9.81 \times 15$, giving $v = 16.3$ ms^{-1}

      (b)   Energy at Q = kinetic energy + potential energy, so 90% of KE at P = KE at Q + PE at Q

            $0.9(\frac{1}{2} \times m \times 16.3^2) = \frac{1}{2}mv^2 + (m \times 9.81 \times 10)$. The m's cancel out, giving $v_Q = 6.55$ ms^{-1}

2.   (a)   Left hand side: Power = energy per second. Units of energy = kg m^2 s^{-2}, so units of power = kg m^2 s^{-3}

            Right hand side: Units of force = kg m s^{-2}. Units of velocity = ms^{-2}, so units on RHS = kg m^2 s^{-3}

      (b)   Velocity is increasing.

      (c)   Time to reach 50 is found using $s = ut + \frac{1}{2}at^2$, $50 = 0 + \frac{1}{2} \times 0.04 \times 9.81 \times t^2$, giving $t = 16$ s

            Maximum velocity is found using $v = u + at$, $= 0 + 0.04 \times 9.81 \times 16 = 6.3$ ms^{-1}

            Maximum power $P = Fv = 1000 \times 9.81 \times 6.3 = 61.8$ kW

            The graph is a straight line passing through the origin and at 16s power = 61.8 kW

3.   Loss of E_P = work done against resistive force

      $50 \times 9.81 \times 10 = 8000 \times d$, giving $d = 0.61$ m

4.   (a)   Gain of E_P = $1500 \times 9.81 \times 2 = 2.94 \times 10^4$ J

      (b)   Efficiency = $\dfrac{2.94 \times 10^4}{6000 \times 8} = 0.61$

(c)   Loss of energy = $(48000 - 2.94 \times 10^4)$ = Force × distance, Force = 9300 N

5.   (a) $v = \sqrt{2gH}$
     (b)   Acceleration is not constant.

6.   (a)   Since force varies linearly from 0 to 1.5 N so F_{ave} = 1.5 ÷ 2 = 0.75 N
           Energy stored = $F_{ave} \times d$ = 0.75 × 0.05 = 3.75×10^{-2} J
     (b) E_K given to cork = 0.8 × 3.75×10^{-2} = 3×10^{-2} J
           $3 \times 10^{-2} = \frac{1}{2}mv^2 = \frac{1}{2} \times 3 \times 10^{-3} \times v^2$, giving v = 4.47 ms^{-1}

7. E_K on entering the water = $\frac{1}{2}mv^2 = \frac{1}{2} \times 50 \times 40^2 = 4.0 \times 10^4$ J
     E_K gained from falling 40 m – 50 × 9.81 × 40 – 1.96×10^4 J
     E_K at top of cliff = $4.0 \times 10^4 - 1.96 \times 10^4 = 2.04 \times 10^4$ J
     $\frac{1}{2}mv^2 = 2.04 \times 10^4$, giving v = 28.6 ms^{-1}

8.   Loss of E_p = work done against opposing force
     0.8 × 150 × 9.81 × 10 = 8500 × d, giving d = 1.38 m

9.   (a)   Resultant force = 5 – 7cos 45 = 0.05 N; work = 0.05 × 2 = 0.1 J
     (b)   Increasing, since the box is accelerating.

10. The difference in height between A and the lowest position of the bob is L – Lcosθ
     The E_K at the lowest position = $\frac{1}{2}mv^2$ = mg(L – Lcosθ), the velocity is given by: $\sqrt{2g(L - Lcos\theta)}$

11. 100 km h^{-1} = 27.8 ms^{-1}
     E_k = work done in stopping = F × 55 J
     $\frac{1}{2}mv^2 = \frac{1}{2} \times 1750 \times 27.8^2$ = F × 55, giving F = 1.23×10^4 N

12. Input power = $\dfrac{8.0 \times 10^4}{0.2}$ = 4.0×10^5 W, i.e. 4.0×10^5 Js^{-1}

     E_k of the water = $\frac{1}{2}mv^2 = \frac{1}{2} \times 50 \times 10^3 \times v^2 = 4.0 \times 10^5$, giving v = 4 ms^{-1}

1.9 Electric current and charge, potential difference and electromotive force

1.   (a)   I = Q÷t = 1.0.2 = 5A
     (b)   Q = Ne, 1 = N × 1.6×10^{-19}, giving N = 6.25×10^{18}
     (c)   As

2.   I = Q÷t = $(3.0 \times 10^{16} \times 1.6 \times 10^{-19})$ ÷ 90 = 53 μA

3.   (a)   I = Q÷t = 25 ÷ 20 = 1.25 A
     (b)   1.25 A = 1.25 Cs^{-1}, 1.25 = N × 1.6×10^{-19} giving N = 7.8×10^{18} electrons

4.   Left hand side, I = amperes A.
     Right hand side, n = number per m^3 i.e. m^{-3}; A = area = m^2; v = velocity i.e. ms^{-1}; e = charge = As
     Multiplying the terms on the right hand side we get m^{-3} × m^2 × ms^{-1} × As = A

5.   (a)   (i) 50×10^{-6} ÷ 1×10^{-3} = 0.05 A
              (ii) 100×10^{-9} ÷ 10×10^{-12} = 1×10^4 A
     (b)   (i)   Q = It = 5 × 5 × 60 = 1500 C
              (ii)   Q = It = $1 \times 10^{-3} \times 10 \times 10^{-6}$ = 1×10^{-8} C

6.   Q = It = 200×10^{-6} × 1 = Ne × 1, N = 1.25×10^{15} electrons

7.   (a)   W = QE = 5 × 9 = 45 J
     (b)   W = QE = 2×10^{-6} × 9 = 18 μJ
     (c)   W = QE = 100×10^{-9} × 9 = 9×10^{-7} J
     (d)   W = QE = $(200 \times 10^{-3} \times 1)$ × 9 = 1.8 J

8.   W = QV, 1.2 = (0.1 × 20) × V, V = 0.6 V

9.   Electromotive force (E.m.f.) and potential difference have the same unit (volt) but they deal with different aspects of electric circuits. E.m.f. deals with a source such as battery that supplies electrical energy. Potential difference deals with the conversion of electrical energy into other forms by a component in a circuit e.g a resistor converting electrical energy into heat. *E.m.f.* is the energy (joules) per unit charge (coulomb) that is converted from chemical, mechanical, or electrical energy into electrical energy in a battery, generator or power supply. *Potential difference* is the electrical energy (joules) per unit charge (coulomb) that is converted into other forms by a component in a circuit.

10. 6 W for 15 × 60 = 5400 J   or W = QE = 6÷9 × 15 × 60 × 9 = 5400 J

11. (a)   work = charge × potential difference = 1.6×10^{-19} × 12 = 1.92×10^{-18} J
     (b)   Energy = QE = $(4.0 \times 10^{18} \times 1.6 \times 10^{-19})$ × 12 = 7.68 J per second = 7.68 W

12. P = IV, 12 = I × 9, I = 1.33 A; 20Ah ÷ 1.33 A = 15 hours

1.10 Resistance and resistivity

1. (a) See diagram. The current flowing into a junction equals the current flowing away from the junction.

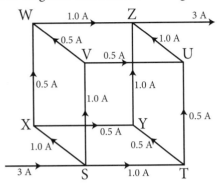

(b) SV to VU to UZ $= 1 \times 6 + 0.5 \times 6 + 1 \times 6 = 15$ V

Resistance $= V \div I = 15 \div 3 = 5\ \Omega$

2. (a) Ωm

(b) $R = \dfrac{\rho L}{A}$

Left hand side: $R = V \div I \rightarrow JC^{-1}A^{-1} = m^2kg\ s^{-3}A^{-1}A^{-1} = m^2kg\ s^{-3}A^{-2}$

Right hand side: $\rho \rightarrow m^3kg\ s^{-3}A^{-2}$; $L \rightarrow m$; $A \rightarrow m^2$; so units of $\dfrac{\rho L}{A} \rightarrow m^3kg\ s^{-3}A^{-2} \times m \times m^{-2} = m^2kg\ s^{-3}A^{-2}$

3. Heating effect or power $P = V^2 \div R$; $P_1 = V^2 \div R_1 = V^2L \div \rho_1$; $P_2 = V^2L \div \rho_2$ Since $\rho_1 > \rho_2$ we can deduce that $P_2 > P_1$

4. Three bulbs in parallel $R_{total} = 30 \div 3 = 10\ \Omega$; $P = V^2 \div R = 12^2 \div 10 = 14.4$ W

5. Conductor e.g. copper $\approx 2 \times 10^{-8}\ \Omega$m

   Insulator e.g. rubber $\approx 1 \times 10^{16}\ \Omega$m

   Semiconductor e.g. silicon $\approx 600\ \Omega$m

6. $A = \pi \times (0.26 \times 10^{-3})^2 \div 4$ m^2; $L = 0.44$ m; $\rho = 5.4 \times 10^{-6}\ \Omega$m

   $R = \dfrac{\rho L}{A} = 44.8\ \Omega$

7. Deal with the 8 Ω and 4 Ω in parallel to give 2.67 Ω

   Then we have 6.0 Ω + 2.67 Ω = 8.67 Ω in parallel with the 10 Ω to give 4.64 Ω (using product÷sum).

   Finally we have 50 Ω and 5 Ω and 4.64 Ω in series to give 59.64 Ω

8. (a) AB: 3 Ω and 1 Ω in series = 4Ω; 2 Ω and 4 Ω in series = 6 Ω; then take the 4 Ω and 6 Ω in parallel = 2.4 Ω

   (b) You will need to sketch the circuit when the 12 V battery is connected across each of the points listed. It will help if you mark the points A to D on your circuit. For example, the circuit when the battery is connected between B and C is shown:

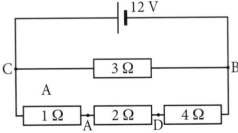

   BC: The 3 Ω is in parallel with 1 Ω, 2 Ω and 4 Ω which are series with each other = 2.1 Ω

   (c) CD = 2.1 Ω

   (d) DA = 1.3 Ω

   (e) BD = 1.6 Ω

   (f) AC = 2.4 Ω

9. The resistance between A and B consist of 4 Ω in parallel with three resistors 3 Ω, 1 Ω and 5 Ω in series giving a total resistance = 2.8 Ω

10. Use $R = \dfrac{\rho L}{A}$. $A = \dfrac{\pi d^2}{4} = 3.141$ m^2 $\times (5 \times 10^{-3})^2 \div 4 = 1.96 \times 10^{-5}$ m^2; $L = 1000$ m; So $R_{steel} = 23.4\ \Omega$ and $R_{Al} = 1.35\ \Omega$.

    Six Aluminium cables in parallel gives a resistance of $1.35 \div 6 = 0.23\ \Omega$

The steel cable is in parallel with the aluminium cables, so total resistance = 0.22 Ω

11. $R = \dfrac{\rho L}{A} = 1.68 \times 10^{-8} \times 3.0 \div (\pi d^2 \div 4) = 4.46 \times 10^{-2}\ \Omega$

12. $A = \dfrac{\rho L}{R} = 5.62 \times 10^{-8} \times 0.8 \div 0.35 = 1.28 \times 10^{-7}\ m^2$. $A = \pi d^2 \div 4$ giving $d = 4.05 \times 10^{-4}\ m$

1.11 Internal resistance and electromotive force

1. (a) V = IR, so I – V ÷ R = 1.55 ÷ (5.2 + 0.8) = 0.26 A
    (b) V = IR = 0.26 × 5.2 = 1.35 V
    (c) $P = I^2R = 0.26^2 \times 0.8 = 0.05\ W$
2. E.m.f. = intercept → 1.5 V, internal resistance = – the gradient → 1.5 ÷ 3.5 = 0.43 Ω
3. Find the current I = V ÷ R = 11.8 ÷ 10 = 1.18 A
    Then find the internal resistance r = V ÷ I = (12.0 – 11.8) ÷ 1.18 = 0.2 ÷ 1.18 = 0.17 Ω
4. (a) Current I = V ÷ R = 6 ÷ (5.0 + 0.500) = 1.09 A,
         Potential difference with 5 Ω resistor = V = IR = 1.09 × (5.0) = 5.45 V
    (b) Current I = V ÷ R = 6 ÷ (500 + 0.500) = 0.012 A,
         Potential difference with 500 Ω resistor = V = IR = 0.012 × (500) = 5.99 V
5. $I = E \div R_{total}$, so $R_{total} = E \div I = 12 \div 0.6 = 20\ \Omega$
    r = 8 Ω (20 Ω – 12 Ω) the internal resistance of each cell = 1 Ω
6. Potential difference across the internal resistance = 12 – 9 = 3.0 V. r = V ÷ I = 3 ÷ 60 = 0.05 Ω
7. E = V + Ir, so we have E = 5.7 + 1.0r [equation 1] and E = 5.4 + 2.0r [equation 2]
    Solving these simultaneous equations gives r = 0.3 Ω and E = 6.0 V
8. E = IR + Ir, so we have E = 1 × 6 + 1 × r [equation 1] and E = 1.5 × 3 + 1.5 × r [equation 2]
    Solving these simultaneous equations gives E = 9.0 V and r = 3.0 Ω.
9. 2000 – 1950 = 50 V difference. I = V ÷ R = 1950 ÷ 8000 = 0.24 A. So r = V ÷ I = 50 ÷ 0.24 = 208 Ω
10. E = V + Ir so we have E = 32 + 3.2×10⁻³ × r [equation 1] and E = 33.9 + 1.695×10⁻³ × r [equation 2]
    Solving these simultaneous equations gives E = 36.0 V
11. (a) I = E ÷ (r + R) = 9.0 ÷ (1.5 + 12.0) = 0.67 A
    (b) $P = I^2R = 0.67^2 \times 12 = 5.39\ W$
    (c) $P = I^2R = 0.67^2 \times 1.5 = 0.67\ W$
12. The required load resistance must be same as the internal resistance (r = 0.5 Ω).
    $\dfrac{1}{2} + \dfrac{1}{R} = 0.5$, giving R = 0.67 Ω.

1.12 Potential dividers

1. (a) The p.d. is divided in the ratio of the resistors i.e. 4 to 1.
         4/5ths across the 40 kΩ is 8 V and 1/5th across the 10 kΩ is 2 V.
    (b) The 10 kΩ voltmeter connected in parallel with the 10 kΩ resistor, giving a total of 5 Ωk. This means the
         circuit is now 40 kΩ in series with 5 kΩ. The ratio of the p.d.s is 8 to 1, so the reading on the voltmeter is now
         1/9th of 10 V = 1.1 V
    (c) $I = V \div R = 1.1 \div 1.0 \times 10^4 = 1.1 \times 10^{-4}\ A$
2. (a)

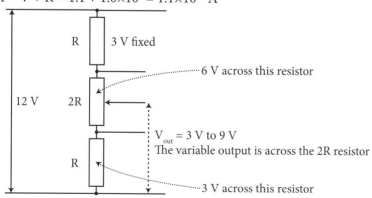

    (b) The resistors should be in the ratio shown eg. 1 kΩ, 2 kΩ,1 kΩ.

3. (a) Using $R = \dfrac{\rho L}{A} = 6.8 \times 10^{-6} \times 0.32 \div 1.2 \times 10^{-6} = 1.8\ \Omega$

    (b) $V_{out} = R_1 \times V_{in} \div (R_1 + R_2) = 1.8 \times 6 \div (1.0 + 1.8) = 3.86\ V$
    (c) As length increases, resistance increases, p.d. increases.

4. (a) $V_{out} = R_1 \times V_{in} \div (R_1 + R_2) = 4\ V$
    (b) Resistance of bulb = 20 Ω, the resistance between A and B is now 19 Ω and
         $V_{out} = 0.52\ V$ so the bulb is dim
    (c) R_1 is 1 Ω in parallel with 20 Ω giving a value of 0.95. $V_{out} = \dfrac{0.95 \times 6}{0.95 \times 0.5} = 3.9\ V$ in normal brightness

5. (a) Dark: ratio of resistances is 500 kΩ to 10 kΩ, so $V_{LDR} = 4.9\ V$; $V_R = 0.1\ V$
         Bright: ratio of resistances is 1 kΩ to 10 kΩ, so $V_{LDR} = 0.45\ V$; $V_R = 4.55\ V$
    (b) Using V = IR: Dark current = 9.8 μA; Bright current = 0.45 mA

6. Calculate the value of R when the output voltage is 4.0 V:
    $4.0 = R \times 6 \div (R + 200)$, giving R = 400 Ω. Therefore ΔR = 1000 − 400 = 600 Ω
    Using the equation ΔR = −16 ΔT, so 600 = 16 ΔT giving Temperature = 37.5°C

7. The total resistance = 2 + 5 + 2 = 9 kΩ.
    The p.d. across each 2 kΩ resistor is 2 V and across the 5 kΩ resistor the p.d. is 5 V.
    This gives an output voltage range of 2 V to 7 V.

8. No current flows when the potential difference at the moveable contact = 4 V.
    The potential across the wire changes by 9 ÷ 50 = 0.18 V per cm.
    Distance to the point at which the p.d. = 4 V = 4 ÷ 0.18 = 22.2 cm.

9. (a) $2.0 = 3\ k\Omega \times 6 \div (3\ k\Omega + R_1)$ giving $R_1 = 6\ k\Omega$
    (b) 3 kΩ and 1 kΩ in parallel gives R = 0.75 kΩ
         $V_{out} = 6 \times 0.75\ k\Omega \div (6\ k\Omega + 0.75\ k\Omega) = 0.67\ V$

10. (a) When load = 47 kΩ, $R_2 = 23.5\ k\Omega$; $V_{out} = 50 \times 23.5\ k\Omega \div (22\ k\Omega + 23.5\ k\Omega) = 25.8\ V$
    (b) When load = 4.7 kΩ, $R_2 = 4.3\ k\Omega$; $V_{out} = 50 \times 4.3\ k\Omega \div (22\ k\Omega + 4.3\ k\Omega) = 8.2\ V$

11. (a) P.d. across the 1 kΩ resistor = 4 V and p.d. across the 4 kΩ resistor = 8 V
         So the voltmeter reads 4 V and Y is at the higher potential.
    (b) The voltmeter reads 0 V when the p.d. across the 1 kΩ and the 4 kΩ resistors = 4 V
         To achieve this, R = 8 kΩ.

12. To find resistance of the bulb: P = IV; 6 = I × 3 giving I = 2 A. Then R = V ÷ I = 3 ÷ 2 = 1.5 Ω. (Or use $P = V^2 \div R$)

    For the 20 Ω resistors, first find the value of R_1 if $R_2 = 20\ \Omega$: $\dfrac{1}{R_1} = \dfrac{1}{20} + \dfrac{1}{1.5}$, giving $R_1 = 0.85\ \Omega$

    Then find the value of $V_{out} = (V_{in} \times R_1) \div (R_1 + R_2) = (6 \times 0.85) \div (0.85 + 20) = 0.24\ V$
    By the same method, the 10 Ω resistors give $V_{out} = 0.69\ V$ and the 0.5 Ω resistors give $V_{out} = 2.6\ V$
    R_1 and $R_2 = 0.5\ \Omega$ is the best choice, since the value of V_{out} is close to the operating voltage of the bulb.

2.1 Waves

1. In transverse waves the vibration of the medium is perpendicular to the direction in which the wave travels. Water and light waves are transverse waves. In longitudinal waves the vibration of the medium is parallel to the direction in which the wave travels. Sound waves are longitudinal waves.

2. (a) $f = v \div \lambda = 3 \times 10^8 \div 600 \times 10^{-9} = 5 \times 10^{14}\ Hz$
    (b) $\lambda = v \div f = 3 \times 10^8 \div 1.5 \times 10^{10} = 2 \times 10^{-2}\ m = 2\ cm$

3. (a) $v = f \lambda = 500 \times 0.68 = 340\ ms^{-1}$
    (b) $\lambda = v \div f = 340 \div 680 = 0.5\ m$

4. From text, $v = k\sqrt{T}$ where   v is the speed of the wave,
                          k is the constant of proportionality and
                          T is the tension
    So, $50 = k\sqrt{36}$, so $k = 50 \div \sqrt{36} = 25/3$
    (a) $100 = (25/3) \times \sqrt{T}$ and hence $\sqrt{T} = 300 \div 25 = 12$
    So $T = 12^2 = 144\ N$
         (Note that this shows that doubling the speed quadruples the tension)
         So the *increase* in tension required is 144 − 36 = 108 N
    (b) $v = k\sqrt{T} = (25/3) \times \sqrt{9} = 25\ ms^{-1}$
         (Note that reducing the tension by a factor of 4, halves the speed.)

5.   (a) $f = 1 \div T = 1 \div 5 = 0.2$ Hz

     (b)   Between the first and seventh peaks there are 6 wavelengths.

         So $\lambda = 63 \div 6 = 10.5$ cm

     (c) $v = f\lambda = 0.2 \times 10.5 = 2.1$ cms^{-1}

6.   (a)   (i)   the maximum vertical distance is 24 cm

         (ii)   the minimum vertical distance is 0.

     (b)   The horizontal distance between two points within the same wavelength which have a phase difference of 90°

         is $\lambda \div 4 = 7.5$ cm

7.   (a)   6 cm $= \lambda \div 4$ corresponds to 90°

     (b)   8 cm $= \lambda \div 3$ corresponds to 120°

     (c)   12 cm $= \lambda \div 2$ corresponds to 180°

8.   Since $f = v \div \lambda$, the 6 cm wave has a frequency of $2400 \div 6 = 400$ Hz

    Similarly, the 8 cm wave has a frequency of $2400 \div 8 = 300$ Hz

    So, the difference in the frequencies of the waves is $400 - 300 = 100$ Hz

9.   Polarised light is light in which the vibrations are confined to a single plane.

10. Sound is a longitudinal wave, so the vibrations are parallel and antiparallel to the direction in which the wave is travelling. So the vibrations are already confined to a single plane, and cannot be further confined.

11. (a) $T = 1 \div f = 1 \div 5 = 0.2$ s.

        Sketch should show 2 complete waves, maximum displacement 4 cm and period of each wave 0.2 s.

     (b) $\lambda = v \div f = 10 \div 5 = 2$ m

        Sketch should show 2 complete waves, maximum displacement 4 cm and wavelength of each wave 2 m.

     (c)   (i)   Phase difference $= 0.8 \div 2$ waves $= 0.4$ waves, which corresponds to an angle of $0.4 \times 360° = 144°$

         (ii)   Distance between points $=$ one wave (2 m) $+ 0.8$ m

             Phase difference $= 0.8 \div 2$ waves $= 0.4$ waves, which again corresponds to an angle of $0.4 \times 360° = 144°$

         {Part (ii) illustrates the fact that a phase difference of $n \times 360° + 144°$, where n is a whole number is the same as a phase difference of 144°}

12. To calculate the speed, we need to find the wavelength. Since the distance between two points is 5 cm and the phase difference is 60°, the wavelength is $(360 \div 60) \times 5$ cm $= 30$ cm. So, $v = f\lambda = 50 \times 30 = 1500$ cm s^{-1} $= 15$ ms^{-1}

2.2 Refraction

1.   (a)   For light travelling from one material to another, the ratio sin i $\div$ sin r is a constant.

     (b)   The refractive index is the value of sin i $\div$ sin r where i is the angle of incidence in air and r is the angle of refraction in the transparent material.

     (c)   Refractive index has no unit.

2.   (a) $\lambda_{air} \div \lambda_{glass} = 1.50$

        $\lambda_{glass} = 600 \div 1.5 = 400$ nm

        $c_{glass} = c_{air} \div 1.50 = 3 \times 10^8 \div 1.5 = 2 \times 10^8$ ms^{-1}

        $f_{glass} = f_{air} = 3 \times 10^8 \div 600 \times 10^{-9} = 5 \times 10^{14}$ Hz

     (b)   sin i $\div$ sin r $= 1.5$

        i$= \sin^{-1}\{\sin(30) \times 1.5\} = 48.6°$

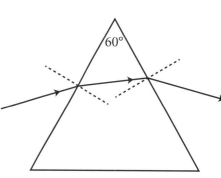

3.   First find r, the angle of refraction in glass:

    $r = \sin^{-1}(\sin(45) \div 1.5) = 28.1°$

    Observe the quadrilateral formed by the two dotted normals and the upper part of the prism. The opposite angles add up to 180°, so the anglebetween the dotted normals inside the prism is 120°.

    Hence the angle of incidence at the glass-air boundary is

    $60° - 28.1° = 31.9°$ (which is less than the critical angle, 41.2°). Hence the angle of refraction in the air is $r = \sin^{-1}(\sin(31.9) \times 1.5) = 52.4°$. So the angle between the ray and the prism is $90° - 52.4° = 37.6°$.

4.   Each wavelength or colour bends by a different angle, because each wavelength travels at a different speed in glass. Red bends least and violet bends most. So, in glass, red light has a lower refractive index, and a higher speed, than all the other colours. So the refractive index for red light in this particular glass is less than 1.52. The refractive index decreases with increasing wavelength.

5.   The incident ray is not refracted because the angle of incidence is zero. The ray strikes the vertical face with an angle of incidence of 45° and is therefore totally internally reflected. The TIR ray strikes the horizontal face with

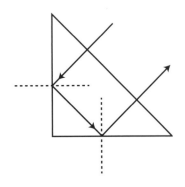

an angle of incidence of 45° and is also totally internally reflected towards the diagonal face. At the diagonal face the angle of incidence is zero, so the ray finally emerges parallel to the incident ray. The angle between the ray that re-emerges into the air and the normal to the surface is zero.

6. (a) The apparatus is shown opposite.
    (b) Method
        1. Place the glass block on a sheet of paper and carefully trace around it.
        2. Remove the glass block and mark the normal at one edge and extend this line into the position of the glass block.
        3. Replace the glass block.
        4. A ray box is used to produce a narrow ray.
        5. Shine the ray into the block so that it meets the block at the point where the normal meets the block.
        6. Mark this path carefully with crosses which are as far apart as possible.
        7. Mark the emergent ray in a similar fashion.
        8. Remove the glass block, join up the crosses to show the incident, refracted and emergent rays.
        9. Using a protractor measure the angles of incidence and refraction.
        10. Carefully replace the glass block and repeat this procedure for a number of incident rays with differing angles of incidence.
    (c) The graph of sin i (y-axis) against sin r (x-axis) is drawn. The straight line through the origin shows that sin i ÷ sin r is a constant and is verification of Snell's Law. The refractive index is the gradient of the line.

7. (a) The angle of incidence at the curved surface of the block is zero, so there is no refraction there.
    (b) The graph shows a (fairly) smooth curve of increasing gradient.
    (c) Extend the curve to obtain the approximate value of θ_p where θ_a is 90°. This approximate value of θ_p where θ_a is 90° is 46°.
    (d) The value of θ_p where θ_a is 90° is the critical angle. So the approximate refractive index is 1/sin 46 = 1.4

8. (a) Critical angle = 90° − 7° = 83°
    (b) Use your answer to part (a) to calculate the refractive index of the cladding with respect to air.
        Critical angle $C = \sin^{-1} (1 \div {}_{cladding}n_{core})$
        ${}_{cladding}n_{core} = 1 \div \sin C = 1 \div \sin 83 = 1.0075$
        ${}_{air}n_{cladding} \times {}_{cladding}n_{core} \times {}_{core}n_{air} = 1$
        ${}_{air}n_{cladding} = 1.530 \div 1.0075 = 1.519$
    (c) By keeping angle θ as small as possible, the difference in the time taken for light to travel up a fibre along the central axis and that travelling in the highest order mode is minimised (modal dispersion is minimised). In the case of an endoscope this minimises blurring of the image; where the optical fibre is used for data transmission, minimising modal dispersion reduces the distortion of the transmitted signal.

9. Critical angle $c = \sin^{-1}(1 \div 1.50) = 41.8°$
    Angle of refraction at first face = 180° − (120° + 41.8°) = 18.2°
    Angle of incidence in air = $\sin^{-1} \{1.50 \times \sin(18.2°)\} = 27.9°$

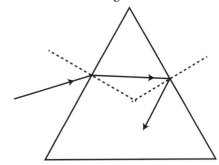

10.

Angle of incidence in air / °	Angle of refraction in glass / °	Speed of light in air / ms⁻¹	Speed of light in glass / ms⁻¹	Wavelength of light in air / nm	Wavelength of light in glass / nm
28	18.0	3×10^8	1.97×10^8	600	395

The frequency of the light is unchanged (5×10^{14} Hz)

11. Refractive index: $_{\text{soft tissue}}n_{\text{bone}} = 1500 \div 4000 = 0.375$

$\sin i_{\text{st}} \div \sin r_{\text{bone}} = 0.375$

$r_{\text{bone}} = \sin^{-1}\{\sin i_{\text{st}} \div 0.375\} = \sin^{-1}\{\sin 10° \div 0.375\} = 27.6°$

12. If the refractive index of the core was less than that of the cladding (1.47) there would always be refraction at the core-cladding boundary. To function, an optical fibre relies on total internal reflection of the signal back into the core when it falls incident at the core-cladding boundary. This could not occur if the cladding had a higher refractive index than the core.

2.3 Part 1 Lenses

1. (a) (i) When parallel rays of light pass through a converging lens they are refracted so that they pass through a point on the principal axis known as the principal focus of the lens.

    (ii) The focal length of a converging lens is the distance between the principal focus and the optical centre of the lens.

   (b)

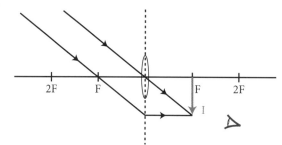

2. The ray diagram (to scale) will look similar to that below.

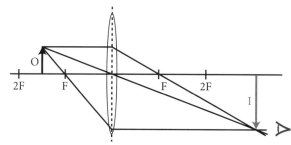

It should show:
(a) the distance between the image and the object is 18 cm
(b) the magnification of the image is 2
(c) the image is real, inverted and magnified

3. (a) $M = \dfrac{v}{u} = 12 \div u = 2$, so u = 6 cm = distance between stamp and lens.

   (b) The image is virtual, so we write: $\dfrac{1}{u} - \dfrac{1}{v} = \dfrac{1}{f}$; so $\dfrac{1}{6} - \dfrac{1}{12} = \dfrac{1}{f}$ and solving gives f = 12 cm

   (c) Since the magnification is 2, the stamp is half the size of the image in every direction. So the stamp measures 2 cm by 2 cm.

   (d) The image is virtual because the stamp (object) was placed between the principal focus and the lens.

4. Originally the object and real image are at 2F on either side of the lens and are the same size. So f = 6 cm.
    When the magnification is 2, v = 2u

   (a) Since the image is real, $\dfrac{1}{u} + \dfrac{1}{v} = \dfrac{1}{f}$, so $\dfrac{1}{u} + \dfrac{1}{2u} = \dfrac{1}{6}$, so $\dfrac{2}{2u} = \dfrac{1}{6}$ giving u = 9 cm.

       So the object must be moved 3 cm closer to the lens.

   (b) Since the image is virtual, $\dfrac{1}{u} - \dfrac{1}{v} = \dfrac{1}{f}$, so $\dfrac{1}{u} - \dfrac{1}{2u} = \dfrac{1}{6}$ and solving gives u = 3 cm and v = 6 cm.

       So the object is moved 9 cm closer to the lens.

5. Since the image is real, $\frac{1}{u} + \frac{1}{v} = \frac{1}{f}$.

   With all distances in mm, we have $\frac{1}{2500} + \frac{1}{v} = \frac{1}{50}$. So: $\frac{1}{v} = \frac{1}{50} - \frac{1}{2500} = \frac{49}{2500}$.

   Giving $v = 2500 \div 49 = 51.0$ mm

6. (a) $P = \frac{1}{f} = \frac{1}{0.4} = +2.5$ D

   (b) $f = \frac{1}{P} = -\frac{1}{4} = -0.25$ m, where the minus sign shows the lens is diverging

7.

Position of Object	Position of Image	Nature of the Image		
		Real/ Virtual	Enlarged/ Diminished	Upright/ Inverted
At F	At ∞	No image	–	I
At ∞	At F	R	D	I
At 2F	At 2F	R	Same size as object	I
Between F and 2F	Beyond 2F	R	E	I
Beyond 2F	Between F and 2F	R	D	I
Between F and the lens	Further from lens than object and on same side of the lens	V	E	U

8. A diverging lens.
9. Since the lens has a negative power, it is diverging.

   (a) $f = \frac{1}{D} = \frac{1}{-5} = -0.2$ m $= -20$ cm

   (b) $\frac{1}{u} - \frac{1}{v} = \frac{1}{f}$, so $\frac{1}{5} - \frac{1}{v} = \frac{1}{-20}$ (where $-\frac{1}{v}$ is used because the image is virtual)

   $\frac{1}{v} = \frac{1}{5} + \frac{1}{20} = \frac{5}{20} = \frac{1}{4}$

   $v = 4$ cm from the lens and on same side as the object. So the distance between object and image is 1 cm.

   (c) $M = \frac{v}{u} = \frac{4}{5} = 0.8$ (the minus sign is ignored when finding M)

   (d) Height of image = M × height of object = 0.8 × 10 = 8 cm
   (e) Image is virtual, erect and diminished.
   (f)

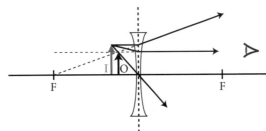

10. (a) and (b)

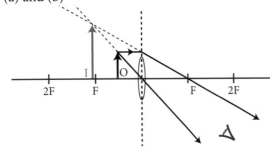

The object is now moved and the image becomes real.

(c) For the image to become real:
  (i)   the object must move to the left so that it is to the left of F;
  (ii) the image will move to the other side of the lens, beyond F.

11. Since $M = \dfrac{v}{u} = 4$, then $v = 4u = 4 \times 20 = 80$ cm

  If the image is real, $\dfrac{1}{u} + \dfrac{1}{v} = \dfrac{1}{f}$

  $$\dfrac{1}{20} + \dfrac{1}{80} = \dfrac{1}{f}$$

  $\dfrac{5}{80} = \dfrac{1}{f}$, so $f = \dfrac{80}{5} = 16$ cm

  If the image is virtual, $\dfrac{1}{20} - \dfrac{1}{80} = \dfrac{1}{f}$

  $\dfrac{3}{80} = \dfrac{1}{f}$, so $f = 26.7$ cm

12. (a) (i)   The images are both real
  (ii) When the lens is in position L_1, the image is larger than the object. When the lens is in position L_2, the image is smaller than the object.

  (b) Rearranging the equation given: $D^2 - d^2 = f. \, 4D$
    Compare this with the equation of a straight line $y \qquad = m \, x \; + c$
    $D^2 - d^2$ corresponds to y, $4D$ corresponds to x and f corresponds to m. So a graph of $D^2 - d^2$ (vertical axis) against $4D$ (horizontal axis) would be a straight line through the $(0,0)$ origin ($c = 0$) with gradient f.

  (c)

D / m	1.00	1.20	1.40	1.60	1.80	2.00
d / m	0.63	0.85	1.06	1.26	1.47	1.67
$D^2 - d^2$ / m^2	0.60	0.72	0.84	0.97	1.08	1.21
4D / m	4.00	4.80	5.60	6.40	7.20	8.00

  (d) The graph is a straight line through $(0,0)$.
  (e) Gradient (from points on line of best fit) $= (1.21 - 0.60) \div (8.00 - 4.00) = 0.15$ m (to 2 d.p.)
  (f) Gradient $= f = 0.15$ m
  (g) When $d = 0$, $D^2 = 4Df$. Dividing both sides of the equation by D, gives $D_{min} = 4f$.
    So $D_{min} = 4 \times 0.15 = 0.60$ m. So the minimum distance between object and screen to obtain a real image is 0.60 m for this lens.

2.3 Part 2 Defects of vision

1. (a) A person who suffers from myopia (short sight) is unable to see distant objects sharply. They cannot make the lens thin enough to view distant objects. This causes the light from distant objects to converge towards a point in front of the retina. The image seen by the person is blurred.

  (b) A person who suffers from hypermetropia (lonsight) sees distant objects clearly but does not see near objects clearly. An object held at the normal near point distance of 25 cm will not be seen clearly. The rays of light from the object are not bent sufficiently to form an image on the retina. The rays converge behind the retina.

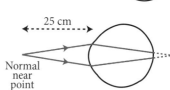

2. (a) Long sight (hypermetropia).
  (b) The eyeball is too short – cornea not curved enough.
  (c) The student's near point is 80 cm. We must find the power of the converging lens that will cause an object at the normal near point (25 cm) to give to virtual image at 80 cm.

  $\dfrac{1}{u} - \dfrac{1}{v} = \dfrac{1}{f}$, so $\dfrac{1}{f} = \dfrac{1}{25} - \dfrac{1}{80} = \dfrac{11}{400} = 36.36$ cm $= 0.3636$ m   Power, $P = \dfrac{1}{f} = 1 \div 0.3636 = +2.75$ D

(d) (i) We need to locate the position of the real object which will give an image at an infinite distance from the lens. But this is the focal length of the lens. So the student's far point is 36.4 cm from his eye.

(ii) The student's range of vision with this lens is 25 cm to 36.4 cm, so an object at 5 m will appear blurred.

3. The patient's near point is 40 cm. We must first find the location of a real object that will give a virtual image at 40 cm with this lens.

Power $P = -0.2D$, $f = \dfrac{1}{P} = \dfrac{-1}{0.2} = -5$ m $= -500$ cm

$\dfrac{1}{u} + \dfrac{1}{v} = \dfrac{1}{f}$, so $\dfrac{1}{u} - \dfrac{1}{40} = \dfrac{-1}{500}$, so $\dfrac{1}{u} = \dfrac{23}{1000}$ giving $u = 43.5$ cm

The patient's far point is 400 cm. We must now find the location of the real object that will give a virtual image at 400 cm.

$\dfrac{1}{u} + \dfrac{1}{v} = \dfrac{1}{f}$, so $\dfrac{1}{u} - \dfrac{1}{400} = \dfrac{-1}{500}$, so $\dfrac{1}{u} = \dfrac{1}{2000}$ giving $u = 2000$ cm $= 20$ m

So with the lens, the patient's range of vision is 43.5 cm to 20 m.

4. (a) When unaccommodated the object distance is infinite, so $\dfrac{1}{u} = 0$.
So the image distance is the focal length of the eye lens.

$F = \dfrac{1}{P} = \dfrac{1}{50} = 0.02$ m $= 2$ cm

(b) $\dfrac{1}{u} + \dfrac{1}{v} = \dfrac{1}{f}$, so $\dfrac{1}{25} + \dfrac{1}{2} = \dfrac{1}{f}$ The distance from the front of the eye (lens) to retina $= 2$ cm

$\dfrac{1}{f} = \dfrac{27}{50}$ cm^{-1} $= \dfrac{2700}{50}$ m^{-1} $= 54$ m^{-1} $P = \dfrac{1}{f} = 54$ D

So the increase in power $= 54 - 50 = +4$ D

5. (a) Myopia (short sight).

(b) The focal length of the prescribed diverging lens, $f = \dfrac{1}{D} = \dfrac{1}{-0.04} = 25$ m. So an object at infinity gives rise to a virtual image at 25 m. The student's far point without glasses is 25 m.

(c) Hypermetropia (long sight). The focal length of the prescribed converging lens, $f = \dfrac{1}{D} = \dfrac{1}{2.5} = 0.4$ m $= 40$ cm
Assume this lens is to give her a normal near point of 25 cm.
So, a real object at 25 cm will give a virtual image at her unaided near point.

$\dfrac{1}{25} - \dfrac{1}{v} = \dfrac{1}{40}$, so $\dfrac{1}{v} = \dfrac{1}{25} - \dfrac{1}{40} = \dfrac{3}{200}$ giving $v = \dfrac{200}{3} = 67$ cm (to nearest cm), which the girl's unaided near point.

6. (a) When viewing an object at the near point, the lens power is a maximum $+60$ D.
Minimum focal length, $f = \dfrac{1}{60}$ metres $= 1.67$ cm

$\dfrac{1}{u} + \dfrac{1}{v} = \dfrac{1}{f}$, so $\dfrac{1}{u} + \dfrac{1}{2} = \dfrac{1}{1.67}$ giving $\dfrac{1}{u} = 0.1$, so $u = 10$ cm $=$ distance from her eye to her near point.

(b) Maximum focal length of eye lens $= \dfrac{1}{55}$ m $= 1.82$ cm

At the greatest distance of distinct vision the power of her eye lens in a minimum.

$\dfrac{1}{u} + \dfrac{1}{2} = \dfrac{1}{1.82}$, so $\dfrac{1}{u} = \dfrac{1}{1.82} - \dfrac{1}{2} = 0.55 - 0.5 = 0.05$, giving $u = 20$ cm. So the child's far point is 20 cm.

The physics student will also note that to focus on objects at infinite distance from the eye requires a lens of focal length equal to the lens-retina separation. In this case that distance is 2 cm. So the child requires to reduce the power of her eye lens to $1 \div 0.02 = +50$ D. But the minimum power of the lens is $+55$ D. So the child is unable to view objects at infinity.

(c) The child suffers from acute short sight.

7. First find the distance between the lens and the retina. When viewing an object at 40 cm:

$\dfrac{1}{40} + \dfrac{1}{v} = \dfrac{55}{100}$, so $\dfrac{1}{v} = \dfrac{21}{40}$ giving $v = 1.90$ cm $=$ distance between the lens and the retina.

Now consider viewing object at 200 cm: $\dfrac{1}{200} + \dfrac{21}{40} = \dfrac{1}{f} = \dfrac{53}{100}$ cm^{-1} $= 53$ m^{-1}. So power of eye lens $= +53$ D.

8. We need to find the power of a lens that will give a virtual image at 1.5 m of a real object at a distance of 30 cm.

$$\frac{1}{30} - \frac{1}{150} = \frac{1}{f}, \text{ so } \frac{1}{f} = \frac{4}{150} \text{ giving } f = \frac{150}{4} \text{ cm} = 37.5 \text{ cm} = 0.375 \text{ m}$$

$$P = \frac{1}{f} = \frac{1}{0.375} = +2.67 \text{ D}$$

9. (a) The patient's near point and far point are both less than that for a healthy eye. The patient is short-sighted.
   (b) We need to find the power of a diverging lens that will give a virtual image at 15 cm of a real object at a distance of 25 cm.

   $$\frac{1}{25} - \frac{1}{15} = \frac{1}{f}, \text{ so } \frac{1}{f} = \frac{-2}{75} \text{ cm}^{-1} = \frac{-200}{75} \text{ m}^{-1}$$

   $$P = \frac{-200}{75} = -2.67 \text{ D}$$

   Note that to see to ∞ the patient needs to use a diverging lens of focal length 450 cm, so its power is −0.22 D.

10. The major problem here is that the far point is 5 m from the eye. We will ignore the fact that that the near point is slightly less than normal. To correct the far point, we need to find the power of a diverging lens that will give a virtual image at 5 m when a real object is at ∞.

$$\frac{1}{\infty} - \frac{1}{5} = \frac{1}{f}, \text{ so } \frac{1}{f} = \frac{-1}{5} \qquad P = \frac{1}{f} = \frac{-1}{5} = -0.2 \text{ D}$$

11. (a) P / D on vertical axis against 1/d / m⁻¹ on horizontal axis
    (b)

P / D	53.33	52.50	51.67	51.43	51.25	51.11	51.00
d / m	0.30	0.40	0.60	0.70	0.80	0.90	1.00
1/d / m⁻¹	3.33	2.50	1.67	1.43	1.25	1.11	1.00

   (c) Graph is a straight line of gradient equal to 1, not passing through (0,0)
   (d) Dioptres (Note that P and 1/d have units m⁻¹, k must have the same unit.) k is the power of the eye lens when the distance d is ∞.
   (e) k = 50 D. It is possible to find k directly from the graph if the horizontal axis (1/d) starts at zero. Otherwise select a point on the graph and substitute the appropriate values to find k.
   (f) 50 D
   (g) The power of the lens is +50 D when viewing objects at infinity. So, $f = \frac{1}{50} \text{ m} = 2 \text{ cm}$

   $$\frac{1}{\infty} + \frac{1}{v} = \frac{1}{2}, \text{ so the retina-lens distance is 2 cm}$$

12. $M = \frac{v}{u} = \frac{2}{60} = \frac{1}{30}$. So the image on the retina is $\frac{1}{30}$ of the real object.

So the image measures $\frac{45}{30}$ cm by $\frac{30}{30}$ cm or 1.5 cm × 1.0 cm

2.4 Part 1 Superposition

1. The Principle of Superposition states that when two waves interfere, the resultant displacement of the medium at any point in space, is the vector sum of the displacements that each wave would cause at that point at that time.
2. (a) In a progressive wave there is a flow of energy in the direction of propagation; no point in the wave is permanently at rest. In a stationary wave there is no flow of energy; certain points, called nodes are permanently at rest.
   (b) Stationary waves are produced by the superposition of two waves, of the same type and having the same amplitude, wavelength and speed, but moving in opposite directions.

3. (a) Ratios (smallest graph first)
        (i)   amplitudes 2:3
        (ii) frequencies 3:1
        (iii) wavelengths 1:3.
    (b) See graph on right.
    (c) The frequency of the resultant wave is the same as that of the larger wave. So its frequency is f ÷ 3.

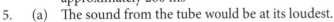

4. (a) Plot graph of v / ms^{-1} (vertical axis) against the square root of the kelvin temperature / K^{½} (horizontal axis). The graph is a straight line through (0,0) confirming the hypothesis.
    (b) Read from the graph the speed when the square root of the kelvin temperature is 16.5. This speed should be approximately 260 ms^{-1}

5. (a) The sound from the tube would be at its loudest.
    (b) Start with the speaker emitting sound at the *lowest possible frequency* allowed by the signal generator. Increase this frequency *slowly* until the intensity of the sound reaches a *maximum*.
    (c) (i)

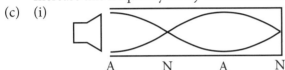

A   N   A   N

        (ii) $3\lambda \div 4 = 30$ cm, so $\lambda = 0.4$ m
        (iii) $v = f\lambda = 850 \times 0.4 = 340$ ms^{-1}
        (iv)   The wavelength remains the same because it is still the 2nd mode of vibration.
               $f = v \div \lambda = 1020 \div 0.4 = 2550$ Hz

6. (a) Graph is a sine wave passing through (0,–2) (2,4) (3.2,3.6) (4,2) (6,–4) (8,–2) (10,4)
    (b) All 3 waves have a period of 8 ms and hence a frequency of 125 Hz
    (c) Time between peaks is 2 ms, corresponding to T ÷ 4. So the phase difference is 90° or $\frac{\pi}{2}$ radians.

7. (a) In the nth mode there are n node-node distances, each of length $\frac{\lambda}{2}$ along the string.
        $L = \frac{n\lambda_n}{2}$, so $\lambda_n = \frac{2L}{n}$. But $f_n = \frac{v}{\lambda_n} = \frac{v}{2L \div n} = \frac{nv}{2L}$
    (b) Graph of f_n against n is a straight line through the origin of gradient $\frac{v}{2L}$.
        Gradient = 28 s^{-1} (to 2 s.f.)
    (c) $v = 2L \times$ gradient $= 2 \times 0.8 \times 28 = 44.8$ ms$^{-1} = 45$ ms^{-1} (to 2 s.f.)

8. Since $L_1 = \frac{\lambda}{4}$ and $L_2 = \frac{3\lambda}{4}$, then by subtraction, $L_2 - L_1 = \frac{3\lambda}{4} - \frac{\lambda}{4} = \frac{\lambda}{2}$

    Hence, $\lambda = 2(L_2 - L_1) = 2 \times 33.2$ cm $= 66.4$ cm $= 0.664$ m
    The speed of sound, $v = f\lambda = 512 \times 0.664 = 340$ ms^{-1}

9. (a) A node in a standing wave is a point which has zero displacement and appears to be permanently at rest.
    (b) There must always be a whole number of node-node distances in the cavity.

        The distance between consecutive nodes is $\frac{\lambda}{2}$.

        If the wavelength is 860 nm, then the distance between consecutive nodes is 430nm. The number of node-node patterns is therefore $0.215 \times 10^{-3} \div 430 \times 10^{-9} = 500$ exactly.
        If the wavelength is 865 nm, then the distance between consecutive nodes is 432.5 nm. The number of node-node patterns is therefore $0.215 \times 10^{-3} \div 432.5 \times 10^{-9} = 497.1$, which is not a whole number. So this wavelength is not possible in the resonant cavity.

10. $\lambda = \frac{v}{f} = \frac{45}{50} = 0.9$ m. The distance between the 3 antinodes corresponds to 1.5 wavelengths.

    Length of wire $= 1.5 \times 0.9 = 1.35$ m

11. (a) The waves travelling from the transmitter to the reflector have the same amplitude, wavelength and frequency as those reflected from the reflector. The waves superpose to produce standing waves. The points of zero intensity are nodes, the points of maximum intensity are antinodes.

(b) The distance between the 1st and 7th successive points of maximum intensity (antinodes) corresponds to 3 wavelengths. So, $3\lambda = 9$ cm and $\lambda = 3$ cm.

$$f = \frac{c}{\lambda} = 3\times10^8 \div 0.03 = 1\times10^{10} \text{ Hz}$$

12. (a) $\lambda = 4(L + e)$

(b) $v = f\lambda = 4f(L + e)$, so $L + e = \dfrac{v}{4f}$. So $L = \dfrac{v}{4f} - e$

(c) Plot L /cm (vertical axis) against f^{-1} / Hz^{-1} (horizontal axis).

The graph is a straight line of gradient $\dfrac{v}{4}$ and intercept $-e$.

(d) The gradient, $\dfrac{v}{4}$, is approximately 8500 cms^{-1}, giving v = 340 ms^{-1}.

The intercept is approximately -2.0 cm, giving e = 2.0 cm.

2.4 Part 2 Interference

1. Rearranging $\lambda = \dfrac{ay}{D}$ gives $\dfrac{D}{a} = \dfrac{y}{\lambda}$

With the violet light, $\dfrac{D}{a} = 600\times10^{-3} \div 400\times10^{-6} = 1.5\times10^3$ which is constant

With the yellow light, $y = \dfrac{\lambda D}{a} = 550\times10^{-9} \times 1.5\times10^3 = 8.25\times10^{-4}$ m = 825 μm

So the separation has increased by 825 μm − 600 μm = 225 μm

2. $\lambda = \dfrac{ay}{D} = 600\times10^{-6} \times 4\times10^{-3} \div 4 = 600\times10^{-9}$ m = 600 nm

3. Sunlight contains all wavelengths in the visible spectrum. For all these wavelengths the path difference between the interfering waves at the point on the axis of symmetry is zero, so they all produce constructive interference there. The combination of all these wavelengths (colours) gives rise to a central, white fringe. However the width of the red fringe is longer than all the others, so the edge of the red fringe can just be seen at the edges of the central fringe.

4. (a) Coherence means there is a constant phase difference between the waves.

(b) Since the phase difference S$_1$ and S$_2$ is zero, they are emitting compressions at exactly the same time.

(c) 180°

(d) $\lambda = \dfrac{v}{f} = 330 \div 1650 = 0.2$ m. Q is the first minimum so path difference = $(n + \tfrac{1}{2})\lambda = \tfrac{1}{2}\lambda = \tfrac{1}{2} \times 0.2 = 0.1$ m

5. (a) Since the path difference to C is zero, the initial phase difference must have been 180°

(b) Fringe width $y = \dfrac{\lambda D}{a} = 600\times10^{-9} \times 4 \div 500\times10^{-6} = 4.8\times10^{-3}$ m

CP is half a fringe width = $\tfrac{1}{2} \times 4.8\times10^{-3}$ m = 2.4 mm

6. (a) Line is straight, through (0,0) origin with gradient 3.0 mm (approx.)

(b) $\dfrac{D}{a} = \dfrac{y}{\lambda} = 5000$, so $\lambda = y \div 5000 = 3.0$ mm $\div 5000 = 6\times10^{-4}$ mm = 600 nm

7. (a) The phase difference between the speakers is 180° so there is a minimum when the path difference at P is zero. At Q the path difference is zero, but because the phase difference at the speakers is 180°, there is a maximum at Q.

(b) The distance y between consecutive maxima is 0.5 m

$$\lambda = \dfrac{ay}{D} = 0.5 \times 0.5 \div 1.25 = 0.2 \text{ m}$$

$$v = f\lambda = 1700 \times 0.2 = 340 \text{ ms}^{-1}$$

(c) A higher frequency note from the speakers means a smaller wavelength.

Since $y = \dfrac{\lambda D}{a}$, reducing the wavelength will reduce the distance y between intensity maxima.

8. (a) 1 cm

(b) Resultant intensity = kA^2 where k is the constant of proportionality. Given that the resultant intensity is I when A = 1 cm, then k = I. So resultant intensity = I A^2.

(c) At the point of constructive interference, A = 2 + 1 = 3 cm. Resultant intensity = I A^2 = I × 3^2 = 9I.

9. The fringes are now green, not red as before. Since green light has a shorter wavelength than red light, the separation of the green fringes is less than that of the red fringes.

10. With the sodium lamp the fringes are often quite faint. Reducing the background light enhances their visibility. With a laser an important safety precaution is keep the pupil of the eye as small as possible to minimise possible damage caused be reflected laser light. Reducing the ambient light causes the size of the pupil to increase and this is undesirable.

11. (a) To obtain maximum separation it is best to use the laser with maximum wavelength, so use the 630 nm laser.
    (b) Maximum slit separation with 630 nm laser,

    $a = \dfrac{\lambda D}{y} = 630 \times 10^{-9} \times 5 \div 4 \times 10^{-3} = 7.875 \times 10^{-4}$ m ≈ 0.79 mm, which can be prepared by the technician.

    With the 511 nm laser, the slit separation must be 0.63875 mm or less, which cannot be prepared by the technician.

12. There are 20 full width fringes seen over the 9.00 mm. Fringe width y = (9.00 ÷ 20) mm = 0.45 mm = 4.5×10^{-4} m

    $\lambda = \dfrac{ay}{D} = 0.95 \times 10^{-3} \times 4.5 \times 10^{-4} \div 0.80 = 5.34375 \times 10^{-7}$ m ≈ 534 nm

2.4 Part 3 Diffraction

1. A larger slit means more energy gets through, so the intensities are all larger; and the width of each peak decreases, so more maxima are observed.

2. (a) d = 1 ÷ N = 1 ÷ 300 mm = 3.33×10^{-6} m
    (b) Max wavelength of visible light is 0.7×10^{-6} m, so slit width > wavelength of visible light.

3. (a) d = 1 ÷ N = 1 ÷ 300 mm = 3.33×10^{-6} m
    Maximum n = {d sin θ ÷ λ) = $3.33 \times 10^{-6} \times 1 \div 600 \times 10^{-9} = 5.556$, so the highest order is 5 since the order must be a whole number.
    (b) The observer sees 5 lines on either side of the central maximum, making 11 in total.

4. (a) d = 1 ÷ N = 1 ÷ 600 mm = 1.667×10^{-6} m
    sin θ = nλ ÷ d = $(1 \times 532 \times 10^{-9}) \div 1.667 \times 10^{-6} = 0.3191$, so θ = $\sin^{-1}(0.3191) = 18.6°$
    The angle between the two 1st order beams = 2 × 18.6 = 37.2°
    (b) Max angle is 90° giving $n_{max} = 3.13$, so the highest observable order is 3. Hence we see 7 laser spots in total.

5. θ = $\tan^{-1}(14.4 \div 75) = 10.9°$
    d = nλ ÷ sin θ = $(1 \times 474 \times 10^{-9} \div \sin 10.9°) = 2.5 \times 10^{-6}$ m
    N = 1 ÷ d = 1 ÷ 2.5×10^{-6} = 400 lines/mm

6. d = 1 ÷ 1200 mm = 8.33×10^{-7} m
    For 589.6 nm: θ = $\sin^{-1}(1 \times 589.6 \times 10^{-9} \div 8.33 \times 10^{-7}) = 45.06°$ (2 d.p.)
    For 589.0 nm: θ = $\sin^{-1}(1 \times 589.0 \times 10^{-9} \div 8.33 \times 10^{-7}) = 45.00°$ (2 d.p.)
    So the angular separation is 45.06° – 45.00° = 0.06°

7. d sin $θ_1$ = $n_1 \times 450$ and d sin$θ_2$ = $n_2 \times 675$ and $θ_1 = θ_2$
    $n_1 \div n_2 = 675 \div 450 = 3 \div 2$
    So, 3rd order for blue light (450 nm) and 2nd order for red light (675 nm) coincide.

8. (a) Infrared
    (b) d = (10 + 7.5) = 17.5 μm
    (c) θ = $\sin^{-1}(nλ \div d) = \sin^{-1}(2 \times 3 \times 10^{-6} \div 17.5 \times 10^{-6}) = 20.05°$
    So the angular separation is 2 × 20.05° = 40.1°

9.

Angle of diffraction, θ / °	8.60	17.5	26.7	36.9	48.6	64.2
Order n	1	2	3	4	5	6
Sin (θ / °)	0.150	0.301	0.449	0.600	0.750	0.900

(a) Plot sin (θ / °) against the order, n and draw the line of best fit. Note carefully the labelling on the axes – this must be the same as in the table.
(b) The gradient of the graph is 0.15.
(c) The gradient has no unit.
(d) Gradient = λ ÷ d, so 0.15 = 600 ÷ d, hence d = 600 ÷ 0.15 = 4000 nm = 4 μm
(e) Extend line to point where sin (θ / °) = 1. Read from here the maximum value of n. This value is 6.7. So the highest order is 6.

10. (a) d = 1 ÷ N = 1 ÷ 500 = 0.002 mm = 2×10^{-6} m
λ = d sin θ ÷ n = $2\times10^{-6} \times \sin(39.3) \div 2 = 633$ μm
(b) θ = $\sin^{-1}(n\lambda \div d) = \sin^{-1}(3 \times 633\times10^{-9} \div 2\times10^{-6}) = 71.7°$
(c) Young's slits are much further apart than the slits in the diffraction grating.
11. d = 25 ÷ 10 000 mm = 2.5×10^{-6} m
λ = d sin θ ÷ n = $2.5\times10^{-6} \times \sin(14.7) \div 1 = 634$ μm
12. d = nλ ÷ sin θ. Minimum value of d = n × minimum value of λ ÷ maximum value of sin θ
= $2 \times 410\times10^{-9} \div 1 = 820$ nm

2.5 Quantum physics

1. (a) Light only exists in packets of discrete energy which depend on its frequency.
(b) E = hc÷λ = $(6.63\times10^{-34} \times 3\times10^{8}) \div 600\times10^{-9} = 3.315\times10^{-19}$ J

2.

Speed in air / ms^{-1}	Wavelength / m	Energy / J	Energy / eV	Part of em spectrum to which this quantum belongs
3×10^{8}	3×10^{-7}	6.63×10^{-19}	4.14	ultraviolet

3. (a) The work function is the *minimum* energy needed to remove an electron from the surface of a material (and take it to an infinite distance from the material).
(b) fo = W ÷ h = $(2.28 \times 1.6\times10^{-19}) \div 6.63\times10^{-34} = 5.50\times10^{14}$ Hz
(c) $hf = W + \frac{1}{2} mv^2$, so $h(c÷\lambda) = W + \frac{1}{2} mv^2$
$6.63\times10^{-34} \times (3\times10^{8} \div 500\times10^{-9}) = (2.28 \times 1.6\times10^{-19}) - \frac{1}{2} mv^2$
So $\frac{1}{2} mv^2 = 3.978\times10^{-19} - 3.648\times10^{-19} = 3.3\times10^{-20}$
Hence v = $\sqrt{6.6\times10^{-20} \div 9.11\times10^{-31}} = 2.69\times10^{5}$ ms^{-1}
(d) Many electrons are liberated from atoms which are several atomic diameters beneath the surface. As they travel towards the surface these electrons lose kinetic energy in collisions with the atoms in the metal lattice. Only those electrons liberated from atoms on the surface will have maximum kinetic energy.
4. (a) Each photon has energy h(c÷λ) = $6.63\times10^{-34} \times (3\times10^{8} \div 400\times10^{-9}) = 4.9725\times10^{-19}$ J
Power of beam = 0.5 Js^{-1}. Number of photons arriving per second = $0.5 \div 4.9725\times10^{-19} = 1.006\times10^{18}$
(b) W = h(c÷λ) = $6.63\times10^{-34} \times (3\times10^{8} \div 5\times10^{-7}) = 3.978\times10^{-19}$ J = 2.49 eV
(c) Number of electrons liberated per second = 1.006×10^{18}
Charge liberated per second = $1.006\times10^{18} \times 1.6\times10^{-19} = 0.161$ A
5. No current would be detected. The incident frequency is less than the threshold frequency.
6. $\frac{1}{2} mv^2 = hf - W = h(c÷\lambda) - W = 6.63\times10^{-34} \times (3\times10^{8} \div 400\times10^{-9}) - (2.1 \times 1.6\times10^{-19})$
= $(4.9745 - 3.36) \times10^{-19} = 1.6145\times10^{-19} \approx 1.61\times10^{-19}$ J
7. (a) Light Amplification by Stimulated Emission of Radiation
(b) (i) The ground is the state of lowest energy.
(ii) An excited state is a state with energy greater than the ground state.
(iii) Normally there are many more electrons in the ground state of the atoms than in the excited states. A population inversion reverses this so that there are many more electrons in the excited state(s) than in the ground state.
(iv) Optical pumping refers to the process by which a population inversion is achieved.
(v) Electrons can only exist in an excited state for a short time before they relax to a state of lower energy. A metastable state is one in which electrons can exist for much longer than in a normal excited state.
(c) Power density = Power ÷ Area = $(1\times10^{-3}) \div (\pi \times (1\times10^{-3})^2) = 318$ W m^{-2}
Comment: This is a much greater power density than that from a normal lamp and explains why looking directly into a laser beam can cause permanent eye damage.
8. (a) Energy must be supplied to an electron in any of these states to ionise the atom and give the electron zero energy; so each state is one of negative energy.
(b) −13.6 eV (the lowest energy state)
(c) Minimum energy transition is 3.4 − 1.5 = 1.9 eV = 3.04×10^{-19} J
Maximum wavelength = hc÷E = $(6.63\times10^{-34} \times 3\times10^{8}) \div 3.04\times10^{-19} = 654$ nm
Maximum energy transition is 3.4 − 0.54 = 2.86 eV = 4.576×10^{-19} J
Minimum wavelength = hc÷E = $(6.63\times10^{-34} \times 3\times10^{8}) \div 4.576\times10^{-19} = 435$ nm
So all wavelengths are in the range 435 − 654 nm; but the range of visible light is 400 − 700 nm.
So all transitions to −3.4 eV result in a photon in the visible region.
(d) 4 + 3 + 2 + 1 = 10 possible transitions.

9. (a) Most of the incident electrons' energy is converted into heat; to dissipate that heat requires a good conductor. The target will become very hot; if it is not to melt it must have a high melting point temperature.
   (b) The transitions between the levels must be large enough to be in the X-ray energy range; this is so for copper, but not aluminium.
   (c) Incident electrons are rapidly decelerated as they approach the target atoms. They lose their KE in a series of collisions. The lost KE is converted to X-rays.
   (d) Electrons in the target atoms may be ejected by collisions with the incident electrons. Electrons in higher energy states then relax to fill the vacancies left by ejected electrons. As they relax, X-rays are emitted.

10. (a) The approximate range of X-ray wavelengths is from 10 nm (1×10^{-8} m) to about 0.01 nm (1×10^{-11} m).
    (b) $\lambda = hc \div E = (6.63\times10^{-34} \times 3\times10^{8}) \div (10\times10^{3} \times 1.6\times10^{-19}) = 0.124$ nm

11. (a) Computed Tomography
    (b) Both use X-rays.
    (c) CT scans give the patient a much greater dose than he would get from a conventional X-ray.
    (d) To protect the patient's reproductive organs against damage from X-ray absorption.
    (e) A computer is required to build up a 3D image in tomography; a conventional X-ray photograph gives only a 2D image and requires no imaging software.

12. (a) $E_k = hf - W$
    (b) Graph with y-axis intercept of -3.7×10^{-19} J
    (c) Gradient = $(9.2\times10^{-20} - 2.6\times10^{-20}) \div (7.0\times10^{14} - 6.0\times10^{14}) = 6.6\times10^{-34}$ Js
    (d) h = gradient = 6.6×10^{-34} Js
    (e) The value of E_k when f = 0 is -3.7×10^{-19} J and is the negative value of the metal's work function. So the work function is 3.7×10^{-19} J.

2.6 Wave-particle duality

1. Particle-wave duality refers to the fact that particles with momentum sometimes exhibit wave properties, while in certain phenomena waves exhibit the properties of particles.

2.
Observation	Refraction	Polarisation	Diffraction of light	Photoelectric effect	Young's fringes
Wave Model	✔	✔	✔		✔
Particle Model	✔			✔	

3. (a) The diffraction pattern showed a series of concentric rings.
   (b) The electrons were being diffracted as they passed between the spaces separating the planes of the atoms.
   (c) The faster the electrons, the smaller is their wavelength. The electrons had to be fast enough for their de Broglie wavelength to be comparable to the spacing between the atomic planes in the target metal.
   (d) X-rays

4. (a) $\lambda = h \div p$ The wavelength, λ, relates to the wavelike nature of the electrons; the momentum, p, relates to their particle nature.
   (b)

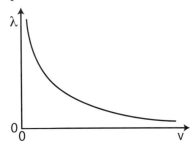

5. (a) Electrons have the longer wavelength.
   (b) $\lambda_e = (h \div mv)_e$ and $\lambda_p = (h \div mv)_p$
       So, since the particles have the same velocity, dividing one equation by the other gives:
       $(\lambda_e \div \lambda_p) = (m_p \div m_e) = (1.67\times10^{-27} \div 9.11\times10^{-31}) = 1833$

6. (a) $\lambda_e = (h \div mv)_e$, so $v_e = (h \div m\lambda)_e = 5.965\times10^{6}$ ms^{-1}
   (b) KE = ½ mv^2 = ½ $\times 9.11\times10^{-31} \times (5.965\times10^{6})^2 = 1.621\times10^{-17}$ J
   (c) KE = $(1.621\times10^{-17} \div 1.6\times10^{-19})$ eV = 101 eV, so the pd = 101 volts

7. $p = h \div \lambda = hf \div c = (6.63\times10^{-34} \times 5\times10^{14}) \div (3\times10^{8}) = 1.105\times10^{-27}$ Ns

8. The momentum of the car is so large (12000 Ns), and its wavelength is so small (5.525×10^{-38} m) that wave-like properties cannot be observed.

9. $100 \text{ eV} = 1.6 \times 10^{-17} \text{ J}$
    $v = \sqrt{2 \times (KE \div m)} = \sqrt{2 \times 1.6 \times 10^{-17} \div 9.11 \times 10^{-31}} = 5.927 \times 10^6 \text{ ms}^{-1}$
    $\lambda = h \div mv = (6.63 \times 10^{-34}) \div (9.11 \times 10^{-31} \times 5.927 \times 10^6) = 0.123 \text{ nm}$

10. $m = h \div \lambda v = (6.63 \times 10^{-34}) \div (2.42 \times 10^{-6} \times 300) = 9.13 \times 10^{-31} \text{ kg}$
    This mass is so close to that of the electron (9.11×10^{-31} kg), that the particle is almost certainly an electron.

11. $E = \frac{1}{2} mv^2$, so $2mE = m^2v^2$ and $p = mv = \sqrt{2mE}$
    $\lambda = h \div p = h \div \sqrt{2mE}$

12. (a) Since $\lambda = h \div mv$, plot graph of λ / m (vertical axis) against v^{-1} / sm^{-1} (horizontal axis). The graph is a straight line through the origin with gradient $h \div m$, where h is Planck's constant and m is the particle's mass.
    (b) Gradient $\approx 7.283 \times 10^{-4}$ J.s.kg^{-1}, so $m = h \div$ gradient $= 6.63 \times 10^{-34} \div 7.283 \times 10^{-4} = 9.10 \times 10^{-31}$ kg
    (c) The particle is an electron (mass of electron = 9.11×10^{-31} kg)

2.7 Astronomy

1. (a) $f = \left(\dfrac{v_w}{v_w + v_s}\right) f_o$, so $660 = \left(\dfrac{330}{330 - v_s}\right) \times 600$. Dividing by 330 gives: $2 = \left(\dfrac{600}{330 - v_s}\right) \times 600$, so $v_s = 30 \text{ ms}^{-1}$

    Alternatively, $\lambda_{source} = 330 \div 600 = 0.55 \text{ m}$ and $\lambda_{detected} = 330 \div 660 = 0.50 \text{ m}$, so $\Delta\lambda = 0.05 \text{ m}$

    So, $v = v_{sound} \, \Delta\lambda \div \lambda = \dfrac{330 \times 0.05}{0.55} = 30 \text{ ms}^{-1}$ (approaching)

    (b) $f = \left(\dfrac{v_w}{v_w + v_s}\right) f_o$, so $f = \left(\dfrac{330}{330 + 30}\right) \times 600 = 550 \text{ Hz}$

    Alternatively, $\Delta\lambda = 0.05 \text{ m}$, so $\lambda = 0.55 + 0.05 = 0.60 \text{ m}$, so $f = v \div \lambda = 330 \div 0.6 = 550 \text{ Hz}$

2. Maximum frequency: $f = \left(\dfrac{v_w}{v_w + v_s}\right) f_o$, so $f = \left(\dfrac{330}{330 - 2}\right) \times 250 = 251.52 \approx 252 \text{ Hz}$

    Minimum frequency: $f = \left(\dfrac{v_w}{v_w + v_s}\right) f_o$, so $f = \left(\dfrac{330}{330 + 2}\right) \times 250 = 248.49 \approx 248 \text{ Hz}$

    Alternatively, $\lambda_s = 330 \div 250 = 1.32 \text{ m}$ and $\Delta\lambda = (\pm 2 \times 1.32) \div 330 = 0.008 \text{ m}$
    $\lambda = 1.32 + 0.008 = 1.328 \text{ m}$, gives $f = v \div \lambda = 330 \div 1.328 = 248.49 \text{ m} \approx 248 \text{ Hz}$
    $\lambda = 1.32 - 0.008 = 1.312 \text{ m}$, gives $f = v \div \lambda = 330 \div 1.312 = 251.52 \text{ m} \approx 252 \text{ Hz}$

3. Note that here the velocity of the source is negative because Andromeda is moving towards the Earth. This is quite unusual for galaxies.
    $\lambda = \left(1 + \dfrac{v_s}{v_w}\right) \lambda_o = \left(1 - \dfrac{110}{300000}\right) \times 656.0 = 655.8 \text{ nm}$

4. Age of universe $= 20 \times 10^9 \times 3.16 \times 10^7 \text{ s} = 6.32 \times 10^{17} \text{ s}$
    $H = 1 \div$ Age of universe $= (6.32 \times 10^{17})^{-1} = 1.58 \times 10^{-18} \text{ s}^{-1}$

5. λ (on Earth) $= 486.1 \times 10^{-9} + 3.2 \times 10^{-12} = 486.1032 \times 10^{-9} \text{ m}$
    $\lambda = \left(1 + \dfrac{v_s}{v_w}\right) \lambda_o = \left(1 - \dfrac{486.1032 \times 10^{-9}}{486.1 \times 10^{-9}}\right) = v_s \div 3 \times 10^8$

    So $v_s = 6.683 \times 10^{-6} \times 3 \times 10^8 = 1974 \text{ ms}^{-1} \approx 2 \text{ kms}^{-1}$

6. (a) By Hubble's Law: $d = v \div H_o = 3.6 \times 10^5 \div 2.4 \times 10^{-18} = 1.5 \times 10^{23} \text{ m} = 1.5 \times 10^{20} \text{ km}$
    (b) $z = v \div c = 3.6 \times 10^5 \div 3 \times 10^8 = 1.2 \times 10^{-3} = 0.0012$

7. The equation given is only valid if $v \ll c$. In this case the calculated speed of the quasar would be greater than the speed of light in space.

8. (a) $v = zc = 0.4 \times 3 \times 10^8 = 1.2 \times 10^8 \text{ ms}^{-1}$
    (b) $d = v \div H_o = 1.2 \times 10^8 \div 2.4 \times 10^{-18} = 5 \times 10^{25} \text{ m}$
    $d = 5 \times 10^{25} \div 9.5 \times 10^{15} = 5.3 \text{ billion light years}$
    (c) Answers to (a) and (b) are only estimates because the equation $v = zc$ is only valid if $v \ll c$, which is not true here where the speed, v, is 40% of the speed of light.

9. Use of $t = 1 \div H_o$ to measure the age of the universe depends on H_o being constant over the entire lifetime of the universe. So, for the early universe, the Hubble parameter was much bigger than our current value. If, in the past, the universe was expanding more rapidly than it is today, we have overestimated the time it has taken for the universe to get to its present size. Our estimate of the universe's age is too big.

10. Consider one of the stars. As it orbits there will be times when it is moving away from the Earth, so its light is red-shifted. At other times when it is moving towards Earth, its light is blue-shifted.

11. (a) and (b) Here we have two unknowns, the speed of the aeroplane, v and the frequency of the sound it emits, f_s.

On approach: $f = \left(\dfrac{v_w}{v_w + v_s}\right)f_s$, so $220 = \left(\dfrac{330}{330 - v}\right) \times f_s$ On recession: $110 = \left(\dfrac{330}{330 + v}\right) \times f_s$

Dividing one equation by the other: $2 = \left(\dfrac{330 + v}{330 - v}\right)$, which after a little algebra gives $v = 110$ ms^{-1}.

Substituting in the first equation gives, $f_s = \left(\dfrac{220 \times 220}{330}\right) = 147$ Hz

Assumption: wind speed << aeroplane's speed.

12. (b) Gradient is approx 2.3×10^5 ms^{-2}
   (c) $f = \left(\dfrac{v_w}{v_w + v}\right)f_o$, so $\dfrac{1}{f} = \left(\dfrac{v_w + v}{v_w}\right)\dfrac{1}{f_o}$. Therefore $\dfrac{f_o}{f} = \left(1 + \dfrac{v}{v_w}\right)$, giving $v = v_w \times \dfrac{f_o}{f} - v_w$
   (d) Gradient = $v_w f_o$ giving a value for v of approximately 338 ± 5 ms^{-1}

Practical Techniques and Data Analysis

1. (a) LHS (force) = kg ms^{-2} RHS = kg m^{-3} × (ms^{-1})^2 × m^2 = kg ms^{-2}
   (b) Drag force (vertical axis) against velocity^2 (horizontal axis).
   (c) See graph on right. The gradient of the F_D vs v^2 graph gives the drag area. The gradient for the Land Rover should be 2.8 times that for the Toyota ($1.62 \div 0.58$) = 2.8.

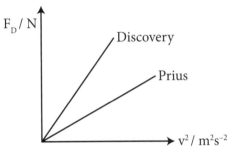

2. (a) $F \times D + W \times 1 = 2 \times T$ giving $FD + W = 2T$
   (b) Dependent variable is the tension T, independent variable is D
   (c) $2T = FD + W$. Comparing this to the equation of a straight line, $y = mx + c$, shows that we plot 2T on the vertical axis and D on the horizontal axis.
   (d) See graph on right.
   (e) The gradient = F, and the intercept of the y axis = W.

3. (a) $mgH = Fs$, giving $s = mgH \div F$. So we plot s on the y-axis and H on the x-axis. See graph on the right.
   (b) From the graph, gradient = 2.2.
   We know that F = 0.8 N and g = 9.81
   Gradient = $mg \div F$, where m = mass of trolley
   Therefore $2.2 = m \times 9.81 \div 0.8$, giving m = 0.18 kg = 180 g

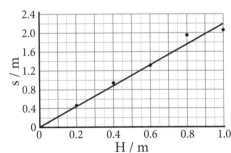

4. (a)

A	B	V_A	V_B
1	1	0	1
1	50	−0.9608	0.0392
1	100	−0.9802	0.0198
1	150	−0.9868	0.0132
1	200	−0.9900	0.0100
1	250	−0.9920	0.0080
1	300	−0.9934	0.0066
1	1000	−0.9980	0.0020

   (b) When masses = 1 kg, A stops and B moves to the right with A's initial velocity.
   (c) A moves back to the left (negative velocity).
   (d) A moves back to the left with a negative velocity equal to original positive velocity.

5. (a) Good experimental practice to improve the reliability of measurements.
    (b) $S = uT + \frac{1}{2}aT^2$ so plot S on the y-axis and T^2 on the x-axis.

S/cm	20	40	60	80	100
T/s	3.7	5.2	6.3	7.3	8.2
T^2/s^2	14	27	40	53	67

See graph on the right. You could also plot S against $\frac{1}{2}T^2$
to give the gradient = 1
    (c) Gradient = 1.49 = $\frac{1}{2}$a, giving a= 2.98 cms^{-2}

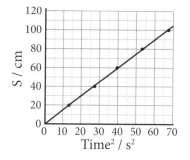

6. (a) Use $v^2 = u^2 + 2aS$, with $u = 0$

S/m	0.15	0.30	0.45	0.60	0.75
V/ms^{-1}	1.20	1.65	2.00	2.35	2.60
V^2/m^2s^{-2}	1.44	2.72	4.0	5.52	6.76

See graph on the right.
    (b) Gradient = 2 × acceleration = 9.0
         Acceleration down the slope = 4.5 ms^{-2}

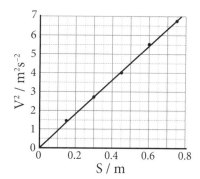

7. (a) Component of the weight down the slope causes the acceleration,
         i.e. mg sinθ
    (b) mg sinθ = ma, so a = g sinθ. Using $v^2 = u^2 + 2as$ with $u = 0$
         gives $v^2 = 2sg\ sinθ$
    (c) Plot sinθ on the x-axis and v^2 on the y-axis.
         The gradient = 2gs and s = 2.0 m.

θ/degrees	5	10	15	20	25
V/ms^{-1}	1.8	2.5	3.1	3.5	3.9
Sinθ	0.087	0.174	0.259	0.342	0.423
V^2/m^2s^{-2}	3.2	6.2	9.6	12	15

See graph on the right.
    (d) Gradient = 36 (from the graph)
         Using $v^2 = u^2 + 2as$ with $u = 0$, a = g sinθ and s = 2.0 m
         giving $v^2 = 4g\ sinθ$
         Gradient = 4g, therefore g = 9.0 ms^{-2}

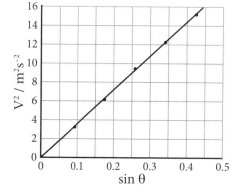

8. (a) For N equal resistors, of value R, in parallel $R_T = R \div N$
    (b) $I = \dfrac{V}{R_T} = \dfrac{V}{R \div N} = \dfrac{VN}{R}$
    (c) Independent variable is N and the dependent variable is I.
    (d) See graph on the right.
    (e) Gradient = $\dfrac{V}{R}$, so R can be found if V is known.

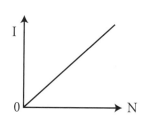

9. (a) For N equal resistors, of value R, in series $R_T = NR$
    (b) $I = \dfrac{V}{R_T} = \dfrac{V}{NR}$
    (c) Independent variable is N and the dependent variable is I.
    (d) See graph on the right.
    (e) $I = \dfrac{1}{N} \times \dfrac{V}{R}$, so gradient = $\dfrac{V}{R}$. R can be found if V is known.

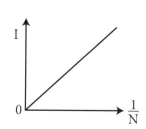

10. (a)

Load R	Power/W
0.1	0.625
0.2	0.918367

0.3	1.054688
0.4	1.111111
0.5	1.125
0.6	1.115702
0.7	1.09375
0.8	1.065089
0.9	1.033163
1	1
1.2	0.934256
1.3	0.902778
1.4	0.872576
1.5	0.84375

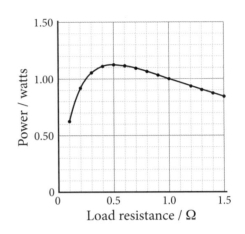

(b) See graph above right.
(c) Power is a maximum when load resistance (0.5 Ω) is same as the internal resistance of the cell.

11. (a) $r_m^2 = (2m + 1)K \rightarrow r_m^2 = 2mK + K$
    (b) See graph on the right. Gradient = 2K and the intercept = K.

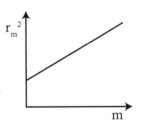

12. (a) Measured value of R = 12.5 kΩ.
    Calculated value = $33.1 - (1.1 \times 20) + (0.014 \times 20^2) = 16.7$ kΩ
    (b) Percentage difference = $(16.7 - 12.5) \times 100 \div 12.5 = 33.6\%$